**FOREWORD BY THE AMEN CLINICS**

# HEALING
## — THE —
# HUMAN
# BRAIN

## A FIRST-HAND USER'S GUIDE FOR REWIRING YOUR MENTAL HEALTH

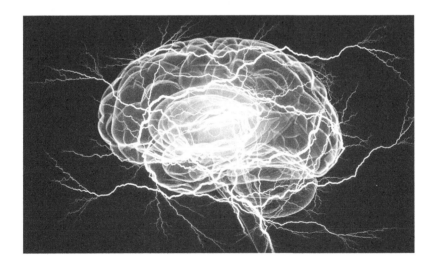

# MICHAEL AND SCOTT WARRICK

IGNITE
PRESS
Fresno, CA

D1593133

Publishing support provided by
Ignite Press
5070 N. Sixth St. #189
Fresno, CA 93710
www.IgnitePress.us

ISBN: 979-8-9850430-3-7
ISBN: 979-8-9850430-4-4 (Hardcover)
ISBN: 979-8-9850430-5-1 (E-book)

For bulk purchase and for booking, contact:

Scott Warrick
scott@scottwarrick.com
www.scottwarrick.com

Library of Congress Control Number: 2022914717

Cover design by Teguh Primada
Edited by Charlie Wormhoudt
Interior design by Jetlaunch

FIRST EDITION

# OTHER BOOKS BY SCOTT WARRICK

*Solve Employee Problems Before They Start:*
*Resolving Conflicts In The Real World*

and

*Living the Five Skills of Tolerance:*
*A User's Manual for Today's World*

This same book is also under the alternative title of
*Tolerance and Diversity for White Guys...and Other Human Beings:*
*Living The FIVE Skills of Tolerance*

*This book is dedicated to my wife Lisa and
sons Michael and Nicholas.*

*Throughout the years, they have had to put up with the best
and the worst of me, the worst of which I hope is behind us.*

*They have also seen me give up countless hours that I should
have spent with them in order to finish my books
and design my various programs.*

*Thanks again, with my apologies and all my love.*

*Scott/Dad*

# Acknowledgments

We (Michael and Scott) would like to acknowledge the Amen Clinics, and more specifically Dr. Charles Parker and Dr. Lillian Somner, for making our mental health progress and this book possible with their cutting-edge neuroscientific approach to healing the human brain. Their willingness to look beyond the standard of care governing the psychiatric profession has changed our lives forever for the better. In this book, we hope to bring our story and message of brain repair to anyone who wants to hear it.

# Disclaimer

The content within this book is not intended to be a substitute for professional medical advice, diagnosis, or treatment. Always seek the advice of your physician or other qualified healthcare provider with any questions you may have regarding a medical condition.

# TABLE OF CONTENTS

# FOREWORD

In the beginning of the book, Scott states that he is not a neuroscientist or a psychiatrist, so you know this book is a personal journey. I love books that share personal journeys.

I am a psychiatrist, board certified, and with decades of experience. I have worked as a psychiatrist in the Amen system for eight years. I am fluent in reading the scans and interpreting what they mean. Michael and Scott do a very good job of explaining the scans in lay language. They clearly show the issues that were seen in their brain scans and also the improvements they were both able to gain from following the Amen protocol.

Michael and Scott go on to describe the importance of good health, overall, in terms of the brain as well as the body and longevity. They have a good grasp of the concepts, and they are able to explain complex material in an easy-to-understand way. They help guide you through things you can do for yourself to build your own brain health program, as well as how to protect your brain from commonplace things that we do that cause damage to the brain unknowingly, how to understand different types of stress and what to do about them, and they make recommendations for a good, healthy approach to psychiatry.

Michael and Scott take you on their journey, through ups and downs, and show you how they were successful in improving their brain functions. It is a worthwhile journey to take along with them.

Lillian Somner, D.O.
Psychiatrist, Amen Clinic
Reston, VA.

# INTRODUCTION

This book is about one thing:

**HOPE.**

Michael and I wrote this book because ...

> **We wanted to prove to the world that we can all rewire our brains, improve our mental conditions, and maybe even cure them.**

No, I am not a psychiatrist. I am not a neuroscientist either. I am much worse. I am an attorney and a father who was scared to death.

When my wife Lisa and I were told in 2001 that our eight-year-old son had Asperger's Syndrome, which is a form of autism, we were devastated. We were told there was little we could do since that was just the way he was born and wired. Rather than relying solely on what our psychiatrists told us, I did my own research. This research opened up a whole new world to me: neuroscience. I soon discovered that neuroscientists were learning more about the human brain now than they had known in the previous 5,000 years. THAT's what I wanted to learn.

Note: At that time, the term and diagnosis of Asperger's Syndrome was used. Today, that term and diagnosis are now referred to as a high functioning form of autism spectrum disorder, or ASD. However, in order to simplify this discussion, and to stay true to this timeline, I will use the term and diagnosis of Asperger's.

Although I had no formal training as a physician or scientist, as an attorney, I had been trained in how to conduct research. After years of intensive research, I eventually discovered:

> **We can all rewire our brains so we can improve our mental state.**
>
> **It depends largely on the choices we all make and understanding how the brain actually works.**

As an attorney, I see everything as requiring proof. If I cannot enter something into evidence in court, I won't make my case around it. I would never rely solely on something anecdotal in my own life, much less my son's. I don't just blindly follow a theory. That is why I researched and cross referenced my findings, which included the workings of the human brain according to modern neuroscience. That also went for my research into the clinical use of nuclear SPECT brain scans. After about four years of researching modern neuroscience and the clinical use of nuclear SPECT brain scans, I took Michael to the Amen Clinics in Reston, Virginia to get scanned in January of 2006. This is where we first met the man who put us on the right track, Dr. Charles Parker.

After Michael returned to school later that month, Lisa and I saw how much better Michael was doing. But then, maybe we were biased and just wanted to see improvement. However, when we met with Michael's teachers, they all asked, "What did you do? He is like a whole new kid."

The truth here is very simple:

> **In addition to the six hours of intake information we gave the Amen Clinic, Dr. Parker also had Michael's nuclear SPECT brain scans to review. As a result, Dr. Parker had a much more complete picture of what was going on in Michael's brain.**

In the end, Dr. Parker was much better able to diagnose Michael's brain issues. This allowed him to more accurately prescribe a better treatment plan for Michael, which included more appropriate medications. The teachers were seeing the immediate impact of Michael's new medication regimen.

After that, I was hooked.

When I was scanned and diagnosed with post-traumatic stress disorder, or PTSD, in 2008, Michael and I both worked on our own brain health programs in order to heal and rewire our brains. We have each had our brains scanned more than once, which not only benchmarked our progress, but also allowed us to recalibrate our individual programs in response to what was happening in our brains.

So, unlike other books on mental and brain health, we now have authenticated photographic evidence showing where our brains have improved thanks to the lifestyle changes we both adopted. So, you will see that everything I am telling you is true.

The improvements in our brains are truly amazing, but it is something most people can also do:

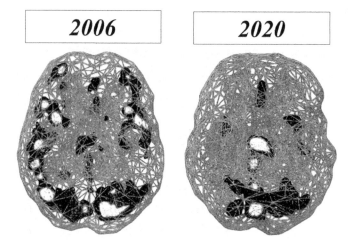

**MICHAEL'S BRAIN SCANS FROM 2006 TO 2020**

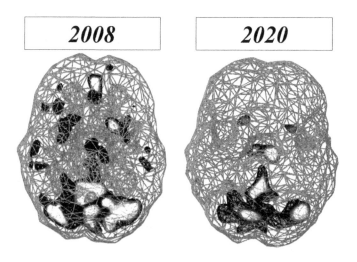

**SCOTT'S BRAIN SCANS FROM 2008 TO 2020**

Without telling you anything about how to read these scans, you can clearly see how much calmer our "after" scans are compared to the ones we originally took years ago. In this book, you will see in great detail the photographs of the before and after conditions of our brains, photographs taken in different years as they were functioning in real time.

This book, *Healing the Human Brain*, is actually the third book in this series. My first book, *Solve Employee Problems Before They Start: Resolving Conflict in the Real World*, tells you how to build your emotional intelligence and how to properly resolve conflicts by using your EPR skills, which stands for Empathic Listening, Parroting, and "Rewards." This is why brain health is such a huge part of my coaching practice. You cannot control your emotions and ego if you are working with a damaged brain. Emotional intelligence **IS** neurology.

To protect your brain, you must also know how to properly handle conflict. Otherwise, you will flood your brain with toxic levels of adrenaline and cortisol, or what we call "distress chemicals."

In my second book, *Living The Five Skills of Tolerance: A User's Manual For Today's World,* I discussed in detail how to build tolerant and "SAFE" environments so we can reduce this epidemic of bullying we see in our workplaces and in our lives. Unfortunately, very few people work everyday in a SAFE environment and it is killing them. If you do not do what is in those first two books, your brain and your body do not stand a chance. All the therapies and medications in the world will not help when you are constantly beating your brain to smithereens with chronic distress.

**After reading this book, you will know:**

- **How to develop your own brain health program in order to repair and rewire it, as well as protect it from further harm.**

- **How we all unknowingly damage our brains every day, and how you can protect your brain, and body, from further harm.**
- **The great difference between the types of stress we all experience.**
- **How today's "standard of care" in psychiatry can actually harm you, and what you need to do about it.**
- **If you or a loved one have been dealing with a mental disorder for years but have not seen significant improvement, why adding a nuclear SPECT brain scan to your diagnostic procedure might help you get better.**

The bottom line?

> **You are not stuck with the brain you've got! It is up to you to change it!**

I often think of how popular superheroes are today in pop culture. Their influence is all around us. I believe one reason they are so popular is because deep down many people wish that some hero would come along and save them from all their misery. However, you don't need a superhero to save you. You have to do it yourself. The power to make your own life better lies deep within yourself if you just follow the simple guidelines we put into this book. You need to be your own superhero.

I truly hope you will take this information I have researched over the last 20 years and apply it to yourself and your loved ones so you can all live better lives.

# 1

## WHAT IS A SPECT SCAN?

In the twenty-first century, we are just now coming out of the stone age of neuroscience.[1] The primary methodology a psychiatrist uses today to diagnose a patient with depression is pretty much the same that Dr. Anson Henry used to diagnose Abraham Lincoln with "melancholy" back in the 1840s.

Today, psychiatrists and psychologists also use lengthy intake questionnaires to help them with this diagnosis. These tests have certainly become helpful and essential tools for psychologists and psychiatrists to more accurately diagnose their patient's conditions. However, the primary standard of care and goal remain the same:

> **Psychiatrists are expected to diagnose and treat patients based on their "symptom clusters" and not on the underlying brain dysfunction.**

Think about it:

> **Psychiatrists are the only medical professionals who rarely see the organ they are treating.**

Based on this diagnosis, psychiatrists will typically prescribe such treatments as medication or a host of other therapies intended to actually alter the way their patient's brain functions. Because there are over 250 kinds of psychological therapies available in the United States, prescribing the right one is extremely difficult.

Also, most mental or brain conditions are not simple disorders. In fact, most people are suffering from multiple disorders. To make this process even more difficult, there are actually different types of the same diagnoses. For instance, there are at least seven types of depression and attention deficit disorder, or ADD. The Amen Clinics have reported that the average patient has over four different diagnoses. So, the psychiatrist's job just got that much harder, if not nearly impossible.

To make matters more complicated, there are dozens of different types of psychiatric medications for the psychiatrist to prescribe. For example, there are over 30 types of antidepressants on the prescription market. So, even if the psychiatrist can accurately diagnose a patient's mental conditions, choosing the right prescription and dosage is another daunting task. What is even more scary is that it has been estimated that 22% of all the medications prescribed in this country are unnecessary.[2]

As a result, most psychiatric medications come with a "black box" warning that says, "Danger if given to the wrong person."

> **Giving the wrong psychiatric
> medication to a patient can be deadly.**

For instance, consider the condition of depression. Psychiatrists incorrectly diagnose their patients with depression thousands of times a day. However, "depression" is *not* a diagnosis. It is a symptom.

Giving patients a diagnosis of depression is like giving them the diagnosis of "chest pains." No physician would ever diagnose a patient with the condition of chest pains because having chest pains is a symptom. Many types of ailments could give someone chest pains, which might include a heart attack, heart arrhythmia, pneumonia or even being hit in the chest by a baseball. Physicians do not give someone the diagnosis of chest pains because it doesn't tell you anything about what is causing the pains or what to do about it.

Now, think about it: If physicians gave everyone who complained of chest pains heart medicine, would some people get better? Yes, some people would. Those people with certain heart conditions would get better because the medication prescribed by the physician just happened to match their condition. However, for many other patients exhibiting the same symptoms, the prescribed treatment would either do nothing to improve their chest pains or they would get worse. Why? Because their symptoms of chest pains were in reality indicating a different underlying condition altogether, which is also the case with many people suffering from depression.

Using a SPECT brain scan could reveal that one person is having **too much activity** in the front part of their brain, which comes from overthinking situations and worrying about them too much. This condition in the brain would most likely cause the person to exhibit symptoms a psychiatrist would classify as depression.

However, another person could be having **too little activity** in this same part of the brain, which could cause this person to be exhibiting the exact same pattern of symptoms as the person with too much activity in this region. In both cases, the patient would be diagnosed with depression. However, according to Dr. Amen, if you treat both of these people in the same manner, you are "inviting disaster."

- If a patient's brain has **too much activity** in certain areas and the psychiatrist prescribes medication that "heats up" those parts of the brain, the result could be disastrous.

- However, if a patient's brain has **too little activity** in those same areas and the psychiatrist prescribes medication that calms those areas down, the depression will get worse. Again, the end result could be disastrous.

So, how could a psychiatrist know what underlying condition might be causing these symptoms of depression? The psychiatrist could order a SPECT brain scan to look and see how these images correlate with the intake data collected from the patient. Such an approach to diagnosing a mental condition is much more thorough and reliable due to the additional information these scans provide.

In one study, board certified psychiatrists were given 109 patient charts to evaluate. Each psychiatrist gave their diagnosis and prescribed treatment for each person. These same psychiatrists were then given the patients' SPECT scans to review as well. The results were astonishing. These psychiatrists:

- Discovered an unexpected brain injury 22.9% of the time,

- They discovered unexpected toxicity 22.9% of the time, and
- They changed their diagnosis and/or treatment plan 78.9% of the time.[3]

When a group of board certified psychiatrists, professionals who are at the top of their field, changed their minds almost 79% of the time when they were given SPECT brain scans to review in addition to the massive amount of symptomatic data they had to consider, that is certainly something I would want to include in my diagnostic and treatment plan.

Interestingly enough, no profession is suffering more from the ill effects of mis- or undiagnosed, or untreated psychiatric disorders than the medical profession itself. Year after year, depending on which poll you examine, the medical profession often ranks very high in the number of people committing suicide. Therefore, few people would benefit more than physicians themselves if the medical profession would take a more neuroscientific approach to diagnosing mental disorders by including SPECT brain scans.

Unfortunately, far too many people today are walking around with mental conditions that have been misdiagnosed, which usually means they have also been prescribed the wrong treatment. These people are forced to struggle with the torturous effects of their mental impairments for years without getting any real relief. We have all met these people, many of us are related to them, or worse yet, often **we are** these people. Either way, it is a tragic sight to see.

# WHAT IS A SPECT SCAN?

**Scott and a SPECT Imaging Machine in 2020
at the Amen Clinic in Reston, Virginia**

What is SPECT? It is an acronym for single-photon emission computerized tomography. It is a sophisticated nuclear medicine study that looks directly at cerebral blood flow and at brain activity. In a SPECT study, a small dose of a radioactive isotope (Tc99m), is combined with Ceretec. Combining Ceretec with the isotope works like a truck hauling a trailer. The Ceretec carries the isotope to the brain, so it acts like the truck hauling the isotope trailer to where it needs to go. Once the Ceretec arrives, the isotope illuminates the brain so the SPECT scan can show its various workings.

The patient then lies on a table for 14 to 16 minutes while a SPECT gamma camera rotates slowly around the patient's head. The camera's special crystals detect the radioactive isotope, which then acts like a beacon of light illuminating the inner workings of the brain. A supercomputer then reconstructs 3-D images of the brain's activity levels. This computer produces elegant high-resolution snapshots of the brain that can provide the clinician with a sophisticated mapping of the brain's blood flow and activity levels. Therefore, a SPECT brain scan will reveal the level of the patient's blood flow throughout the brain and the different levels and patterns of activity.

With these photographs, psychiatrists have been able to better identify certain areas of brain activity and blood flow that correlate with the patient's clinical symptoms. This allows the psychiatrist to ask better questions to determine the true nature of the patient's psychiatric and neurological condition.

For a more in-depth look at the differences between SPECT scans, MRIs, fMRIs and PET scans, just go www.scottwarrick. com and look under the "Healing The Human Brain" section.

Also, I have had a great deal of success getting insurance companies to pay a substantial portion of the SPECT brain scan procedure. Amazingly, still to this day I will have insurance claims adjusters ask if this procedure is for a physical or mental condition. My reply is always the same: "Yes. It's the brain."

You also cannot forget that mental disorders have carried a tremendous social stigma for centuries. We have typically dismissed people with mental problems as being "moonstruck," "looney," "nuts," or just plain "crazy." For years, mental patients were even put on display for the general public to come and view, just like going to the zoo.

Unfortunately, many of these stigmas continue to this day. However, if one understands that every mental disorder is actually a physical disorder in the brain, and if the public could actually see what different mental impairments often look like in the brain, then many of these stigmas would simply disappear. Understanding a condition helps to eliminate stigmas, just as it has with tuberculosis and cancer, whose stigmas have largely disappeared.

And finally, when someone with a mental illness can actually see the problem that exists within their brain, they can much better understand their condition. The person can better understand that they really do have a physical problem with their brain and they need to correct it. Patients are then much more likely to cooperate with their prescribed treatment and comply with their doctor's orders.

It is one thing to tell someone they are suffering from bipolar disorder. It is quite another to show it to them.

## SPECT RESEARCH AND CLINICAL USE

The medical support for using SPECT scans to help physicians better diagnose their patients' brain issues goes back decades. Unfortunately, too many medical practitioners remain unaware of this emerging science that could prove to be a God-send for their patients.

Think of it this way: What would you do if your child fell from a tree and landed on his arm? As the child held his arm and cried, you would rush the child to the hospital. What if instead of ordering an x-ray, the physician looked at your child's arm and manipulated it back into position? Then assume the physician stood back and proudly said, "There. That ought to do it. See . . . it's straight. Let's slap a cast on that and get you home!"

How many lawyers would line up to take that physician's license?

Steve Hyman, director of the National Institute of Mental Health, has noted that psychiatry, arm in arm with neuroscience, is poised to enter a new age, which he calls "the millennium of mind, brain, and behavior." In fact, we have learned more about the human brain since the early 2000s than we have known in the previous 5,000 years.

In short:

1. SPECT scans can help a clinician ask better questions.
2. SPECT scans can help a clinician make a more accurate and complete diagnosis, which includes helping to avoid inaccurate diagnoses and incorrectly prescribed treatments.
3. SPECT scans can play a vital role in reducing the stigma associated with mental disorders.
4. SPECT scans can help motivate patients to cooperate with their treatment plan.

Frankly, it only makes sense:

> **If someone has been suffering from a mental impairment for years and various treatments and medicines have not worked . . . it is time to take a look.**

For a more in-depth look at some of the support these SPECT scans have gotten from the research and medical community, please go to www.scottwarrick.com and look under the "Healing The Human Brain" section for the article on "SPECT Research and Clinical Use."

# 2

## IN THE BEGINNING. . . WHY I CHOSE TO HAVE A SPECT SCAN

### SCOTT'S STORY

In this chapter, I'd like to share some stories from my life to shed light on some of the ways we unwittingly subject our brains to abuse, and the less than ideal strategies we sometimes use to "fix" them. I am sure many of you will relate to these stories, since you have likely experienced these same issues in your own lives. You probably just didn't realize the harm they were inflicting on your body and brain.

I was born on November 24, 1960. However, I also grew up in a time when boys were supposed to be tough. We didn't worry about people's feelings so much. Fighting and bullying were a way of life. It was supposed to get you ready for the real world. Boy, were we ever wrong.

One of the biggest problems with bullying a child is that their brain has not fully formed yet. When we are born, we actually have more neurons in our brains than we need. A child's brain actually has twice as many neurons as an adult's brain. So, to make room for the most important neurons, for the first few years, our brains simply "prune off" the ones it thinks we don't need. Because of the experiences we have in our early years, our brains will wire themselves in response to the experiences we have as children, which includes determining which neurons to keep and which ones to kill off. These experiences will govern how we think for the rest of our lives. Actually, a child's brain becomes "culturally bound" to their surroundings by the age of 11 months.[4]

This explains why we have red states and blue states: It is the culture in which that baby is raised. This also explains why we have cannibals. If you were raised to eat people, common sense would tell you that you don't bury grandpa when he dies . . . you eat him.

What is also important to understand is that a person's brain does not fully form until they are in their mid-20s. When we are born, the neurons in our brain are pretty much unprotected. Think of them as being just bare, uninsulated copper wires.

As the brain matures, these bare neurons become wrapped in a white, fatty substance called the "myelin sheath," which is called "myelination." This is like wrapping those copper wires with insulation, which not only helps to protect our neurons but it also makes them anywhere from **10 to 100 times** more efficient. Myelination starts at the base of our brain and then moves forward as we get older. The myelination of the occipital lobes, which are involved with our vision, begins in the first days of life, which is why babies can see us rather clearly soon after they are born. This myelination process then slowly moves from the base of our brain and on upwards. This is why babies crawl, then walk, and then run. The myelin sheath is moving up and across the child's brain so the neurons are becoming at least ten times more efficient as our strength also increases. It is not until young women turn about 25 years old and young men turn about 28 that the prefrontal cortex, or our frontal lobes located right behind our forehead, become fully myelinated. Yes, this is why you see so many young people do so many stupid things right up to their mid-twenties. Their frontal lobes, or their logical brain, have not fully formed yet.[5]

And yes, girls do mature faster than boys. Sorry guys.

So, when a child is bullied or experiences violence, not only will this affect the wiring in their brain, but they will also go into a state of fight-or-flight. When this happens, their adrenal glands will instantly secrete massive amounts of adrenaline and cortisol throughout their body, and about 20% of those distress chemicals will go right to their brain—which is largely unprotected and unmyelinated. This massive amount of adrenaline and cortisol will burn their little neurons quickly because they just don't have the myelin sheath to protect them. That is why children are particularly susceptible to brain disorders because their unmyelinated neurons can be burned so quickly.[6]

This is also how we adults can get a basket full of mental disorders:

> **These distress chemicals will literally burn our brains.**

That is what happened to me. That is why my mental health issues make such a great comparison to my son, Michael, who was born with Asperger's. I was most likely born with a healthy brain. However, the abusive conditions I subjected myself to in my lifetime damaged it severely, especially as a child. This is true of most people in the world. Today, we unwittingly treat our brains like soccer balls, especially during and after a pandemic.

Michael, on the other hand, was born with his condition, but he was still able to rewire his brain significantly.

I did not know anything about the human brain when I was growing up, or I would have addressed these tragedies in a very different way.

I have never been a big guy. I am definitely on the smaller side. As an adult, I am a towering five foot, six inches tall—and shrinking. That doesn't matter so much anymore, but it did when I was four.

I was bullied and beaten up from a very young age. No one seemed to worry about it all that much. You had to learn how to take it. So, getting ostracized, teased, or beaten up by perhaps an older girl was never something an adult would address. It was embarrassing, so you didn't talk about it. You ignored it.

A couple of years ago, I saw one of my little relatives being bullied by an older cousin. When I stepped in, another adult smiled, then told me,

> **"They're just kids. It's OK."**
> **Whoever says anything like that**
> **is an idiot.**

For me, I acted out. Humor seemed to deflect these feelings of hurt and distress. That explains a lot about who I am today.

When I was in the third grade, my family moved from the east side of Newark, Ohio to the west side where I went to a new school, Cherry Valley Elementary. Now, there is really nothing historically important about Cherry Valley, but it did have one tremendous advantage for me: The brand new Emerson Miller Library had just been built on the school's land.

It was a great library. It had everything, including books about taekwondo, with great pictures and everything. I checked out several books on various martial arts, including jiu jitsu. Considering my size, this was perfect for me.

I taught myself as many martial arts moves as I could remember. The next few times I was attacked, I flipped the other person onto the ground. That was usually the end of it.

As I grew older, the need to physically defend myself and flip people went away. Instead, the emotional bullying began, which was much worse. I later realized that emotional bullying is the type of violence that does us the most harm because you not only relive it in your head late at night, but you are always waiting for the next shoe to drop. I also learned that our body was not designed to deal with psychological attacks. Instead, we humans are designed to deal with physical attacks by using our fight-or-flight response. Our fight or flight response is not designed to deal with emotional bullying. As your brain tortures you with these thoughts of being bullied, your fight-or-flight system will run, then shut off, and then run again later. This psychological distress can damage our brain even when we sleep, which sometimes results in night terrors.

This is the type of bullying most people have to endure every day of their lives, and it is literally killing them.

I am always amused and disgusted by people who say things like, "Well, just don't think about it" or "Don't let that person rent space in your head" or "Just get over it." Clearly, they do not understand OCD, or obsessive-compulsive disorder, or the host of other brain injuries we experience from this flooding of adrenaline and cortisol. Telling someone to "just get over it" when they have OCD is like telling someone with a broken leg to "just walk it off." Treatment, cognitive behavioral therapy, or CBT, medication, and a rewiring of the brain are needed. (I will show you my OCD later. It was not good.)

It was then I developed my wit and my sense of humor. Sarcasm seemed to serve me well. I learned I could disarm many bullies with humor, which is when I first started referring to these bullies as "trolls." It became my primary defense mechanism. Humor is also a skill I use to this day to present very difficult subjects to my audiences.

In 1965, my parents took a road trip to the World's Fair in Queens, New York. Unfortunately, while driving home, they were in a terrible car accident. My dad suffered minor injuries, but my mom suffered several broken bones including her neck and jaw. She would spend several months in the hospital and years recovering. I distinctly remember the large hospital bed that was brought into our living room when she finally made it home.

For months, I bounced around from family member to family member while my mom was away. My little brother, Kelly, stayed with our grandmother. My older sister, Pam, spent much of her time with my uncle's family. We spent a lot of time apart. However, for us, the worst was yet to come.

After she returned home, my mom's doctors tried to manage her pain. However, their answer was to just give her stronger and stronger pain medications. Eventually, she became addicted.

This was all seen as being legitimate. It was the standard of care. Doctors were prescribing these medications for her, so the danger of addiction never occurred to us. We were sure she was in good hands.

This would not be the last time a close family member or I would become the victims of the medical profession and its "standard of care," and most of the bad advice we got was in relation to our brain health.

Throughout my elementary, high school, and college years, my mom was addicted to prescription pain medications, which made victims of not only her, but our entire family. No one ever bothered to look and see if my mom's doctors, and later her psychiatrists, were turning her into a drug addict. They were.

While I was growing up, her behavior was like anyone else addicted to drugs. It could be erratic. Her moods would fluctuate. She was then misdiagnosed with bipolar disorder, resulting in psychiatric hospitalizations, which incorporated electroconvulsive therapy, or ECT. ECT shocks the brain to induce generalized seizure activity, which effectively wiped out portions of her long-term memory. Part of her was now gone forever.

My mom had a history of migraines before the accident, but these medications made them even worse. Due to her addiction, her body was craving more powerful drugs. Soon, rest and painkillers did not do the job. To alleviate her migraines, we had to take her to the emergency room to be injected with more powerful painkillers. She would then spend about three days in bed trying to recover from the migraine. This led to worsening her depression.

I didn't know it then, but I now realize these drugs were playing havoc on her brain. Simply put, your body and brain do not recognize the difference between the drugs you get from a pharmacy and the ones you get from the corner of 5th and Main.

Not until 1983 did a psychologist finally recognize my mom's real problem. She was a drug addict. That was when she went through rehab. After that, she was a new person, but not until traditional medicine stripped away about 20 years of her life.

After rehab, her migraines stopped. She was finally able to participate in her own life again. A critical lesson to learn from this nightmare is that it was a **psychologist** who saved my mom's life from the psychiatrists.

What the psychiatrists and traditional medicine did to my mom was unforgivable. It is not acceptable to say these physicians and psychiatrists were only following the standard medical practices of the time when a psychologist recognized the problem right away.

Now you know why I **always** tell the clients I am coaching that it is not enough to just go to a psychiatrist to get their medications. It is vital that my clients have both a psychologist and a psychiatrist on their medical team. I have found that most psychologists have a much more in-depth understanding and training in human behavior than do most psychiatrists. Today, there is an entire field of neuropsychology, which looks at brain function in relation to our behavior. If my mom had seen a psychologist regularly, her addiction issues would have been diagnosed and addressed much earlier.

This standard of care did not change for years. As many of you realize, we are battling a prescription drug opioid and opiate epidemic in this country. I remember thinking, "They are still at it. That is my mom all over again."

Since then, I have been more than a little skeptical of the "standard of care" used by the medical profession, especially when it comes to brain health. In these types of instances, people get seriously hurt. But then, these are doctors. You follow their advice because, well, they're doctors.

For years, my brain had been flooding with massive amounts of distress chemicals, or adrenaline and cortisol, for various reasons, but the summer of 1977 was an especially tough year for me.

So, one night, I went into my mom's medicine cabinet, took the fullest bottle of sedatives I could find, and swallowed them. I then wrapped the empty bottle in a paper bag and put it in the trash can outside so no one would find it. I then went to bed. I made sure I left no signs. I told no one what I was doing.

However, since it was dark, I took the wrong medicine by mistake. I thought I was taking painkillers and sedatives, but my mom must have also been having intestinal problems, and I ended up swallowing a bottle of medicine for that. Sometime after midnight, I woke up with a searing pain in my lower abdomen, probably my large intestines. I rushed to the bathroom and drained most of the electrolytes out of my body. (I still wonder how that didn't kill me.)

My parents heard me in the bathroom and got out of bed. My dad woke up briefly, but had to go to work the next day, so he went back to bed. My mom handled it. I suppose they thought I was just sick.

This has been my darkest secret for decades. It is not exactly something you put on your bio. I only bring it up now because of what I later experienced with our son, Michael.

It is also important to recognize that the Centers for Disease Control has listed suicide as being a national health crisis, which includes attempted suicides, and it is only getting worse as our world becomes more intolerant. The National Institute of Mental Health has reported that suicide is now one of the leading causes of death in the United States.

I am here to tell you: Take these situations seriously. These are most often serious brain issues that need to be addressed. If you or anyone you know is thinking about suicide, get help. Go to a licensed psychologist or call the National Suicide Prevention Lifeline at 988.

You can also call 911 to deal with an immediate crisis.

We need to kill the stigma of mental issues and look at physically repairing the person's brain. For years, I hid my mental disorder, PTSD, which was not healthy for me or the people around me. I no longer do that. When more people openly acknowledge and discuss these issues, the more these stigmas will die.

Today, I am in my early sixties. If someone wants to attack me by labeling me with another stigma, they will have to get in line.

Later, I worked my way through college. When I finally got the chance to go to law school in my early 30s, I worked all day at a bank in human resources and went to law school at night. Over the next four years, I would terribly damage my health and therefore my brain. Getting good grades was my only focus. It was not my health. I am now paying that price for the rest of my life. Brains can rewire and heal, which is not something you can do with diabetes.

As you will see, the environment we expose our body and brain to will either turn on or shut off many of the various genes in our body. I was born with the diabetes gene, but had I taken care of myself like I do now, I probably would not have diabetes today.

I then made the mistake of working at a couple of different large law firms, which is most law students' dream job. However, this meant I went to work for mostly litigators, the attorneys who try cases. While some litigators do have a soul and are ethical about the practice of law, that is not who I usually worked with. I worked with some of the most arrogant, narcissistic sociopaths (or emotional children) you could ever meet.

These experiences taught me why attorneys commit suicide as often as they do, and why substance abuse is so widespread throughout the legal profession. They are self-medicating. Their constant flooding of adrenaline and cortisol is burning their neurons to bits, and they are doing it to themselves. Many then turn to excessive drinking and drug abuse to calm down their brain.

Today, substance abuse, suicides and mental disorders are out of control in the legal profession. Studies have shown that at least 20% of all attorneys have a drinking or substance abuse problem, while other studies show that over 36% are struggling with alcohol abuse.[7]

What is worse, more than 45% of attorneys experience depression during their career.[8]

According to the National Institute of Mental Health, lawyers are nearly FIVE times more likely to commit suicide than the general population. The only difference is that they can usually afford a better casket.[9]

Honestly, don't let your babies grow up to be litigators. Make them be cowboys.

I later went to work for a consulting company. It was the perfect job for me. I was the in-house legal counsel and the human resource director for all of the company's outside accounts. However, the salary they could afford to pay me was $20,000 less than I was currently making. So, to make it all work, I cut a special deal with the company. I would be allowed to continue my own private employment law and management training practice, which was thriving at the time. To make up for this loss in pay, I was given an additional seven personal days a year so I could conduct training and perform work for my own clients. Between my seven personal days, my regular vacation days and my weekends, I could actually make quite a bit more than what I was losing in salary.

In return, I would be able to join the company, but I would also bring all of my training programs along with me so the company could instantly offer many different seminars for its clients. It was a win-win, right up until the company breached my contract a few years later.

At the same time I started working at the consulting company, Michael's personality changed drastically. Instead of being that outgoing and personable little man who sang and openly greeted everyone he saw, he became withdrawn and isolated. We didn't know what was wrong, so we were going from doctor to doctor desperately trying to find out what was happening to our four-year-old son.

Once I started working for the consulting company, Lisa quit her job as a radiographer to stay at home and focus on our two sons, Michael and his younger brother, Nicholas. We knew we needed to find some answers for Michael, and it was probably going to be expensive. My new job at the consulting company was a God-send.

However, a few years later, I was called into the president's office along with the COO. I was told the company could not honor my contract anymore because it wanted to start selling training programs to the business community. So, all of the income I was earning through my private training practice was gone. Of course, I was not given a raise to make up for my loss of income.

They also told me that I had to load all of my clients' information into their computer system because they owned my client list now. I was no longer allowed to conduct any legal work or training through my private practice to supplement my income.

They summarized everything by telling me, "All of your clients are ours now."

"But my wife quit her job based on this deal," I said. "And we need that extra income to find out what is happening with Michael. This is going to kill us."

Their response was short and to the point. They told me, "That's not our problem."

I instantly broke into a cold sweat. My mind took off in a thousand directions. Who was going to take care of my family? How was I going to pay for the help Michael was going to need? What was I going to do?

At that point, I broke. The fear took complete control of my body and I broke down in tears. I couldn't stop. I didn't know what I was going to do.

"But we have a contract," I explained.

"We cannot honor that anymore. We want to focus on the training part of the business. And you also need to load all of your training programs into our computer system. We own all of your training materials now," they told me.

Of course, I think they saw how popular my training practice was, so they wanted it for themselves. They also knew what I was going through with Michael, so this was the perfect time to strike. I had become vulnerable in their eyes.

Still, I had to make this deal work. So, I offered to give the company a license to use my training programs whenever they wanted, but I could not relinquish the ownership of all my training materials. That would mean that I couldn't use them in the future.

They refused. They claimed they owned all of my training programs because I had been using them for the company during the last few years. They claimed my training programs had entered their "domain," so the company now owned them. They wanted to use them in marketing their new management training programs.

I was stunned. That was the stupidest thing anyone had said to me in years.

As an attorney and HR professional who had written thousands of pages of presentation materials, I knew full well this was not what the law said. I wrote these training materials before I ever joined the company and used them in my training practice. I owned the copyrights and there was no question about that. This was like hiring Steven Spielberg to come to your house to present a showing of *Schindler's List*, and then claiming you now own it because he let you project it onto your barn for movie night.

I cannot tell you how traumatic the next several months were for me as I agonized about what to do. I could not turn over my client list, and I would never give up the ownership of my training programs. My gut clenched for weeks. I couldn't sleep, and when I did fall asleep, I would wake up drenched in sweat. I was getting sick to my stomach in meetings. As you read on, you will see how my brain was already being damaged over this psychological torture. Whenever you start exhibiting these physical symptoms of chronic distress, your brain has already been damaged. Yes, in situations like this, your brain is the first organ to go.

So, I decided to jump off the cliff, figuratively speaking. I quit my job, our sole source of income, and started my own company: Scott Warrick HR Consulting and Employment Law Services. I was risking my family's future, but I didn't see any other option. Suing the company for breach of contract, and for a host of other offenses, would take years to resolve, and Michael needed help now. For the first time in my life, I became a full-time, self-employed employment attorney and professional speaker. I had no idea if it would work, but thank God it did.

So, when someone tells me that they are being bullied at work, BELIEVE ME, I understand, but it is up to you to do something about it.

Unfortunately, I have found that being a professional speaker and author who addresses difficult topics, such as tolerance and mental health, to be just as stressful as being a litigator. To me, we are all humans, and according to the Human Genome Project, we are all related to everyone else on the plant. It is a scientific fact that everyone I meet is my brother, sister, cousin and so on, and that fact drives my passion for all humans. As someone who regularly practices law in the area of civil rights, I am passionate that no one should ever be discriminated against.

Naively, I thought everyone would agree with those sentiments, but it is rare that a week goes by when I don't get attacked for being a White male who teaches tolerance either from the far political left or the far political right. From the far right, I am told that I am not White anymore. From the far left, I am told that tolerance and diversity are strictly racial issues that must only be taught only by someone of color. And just for fun, every so often, one side or the other of the political spectrum will even shoot off to me a death threat.

Actually, a couple of times a month I am told by some organization that they love my tolerance program, but they are only allowed to bring in someone who is Black to present on such topics. Yes, race is an important topic of diversity, but so are mental disabilities, physical disabilities, poverty, sexual orientation and so on. Actually, several studies show that people with disabilities are the most discriminated against group of people in America and throughout the world. That means more people with disabilities who could work if they were given a chance are unemployed. No one would know that Michael or I had a mental disability at first glance. My inclusive stance that diversity encompasses race and anything else that makes us different from one another has brought many attacks my way.

I am also regularly attacked, usually by the people who are running our toxic organizations, for professing that we need to create SAFE work environments for everyone because our bullying workplaces present one of the greatest threats to our mental and physical health. That does not go over well with the so-called leaders running these organizations. One leader at a director's association actually said, "We wouldn't want our people to hear about this. No one will work for us."

Maybe, just maybe, it would be better to convince your employees to help you create a SAFE environment rather than perpetuating a toxic workplace that is killing everyone. It's just a thought.

There is simply no pleasing everyone, so no matter what I say, someone somewhere will be upset, which usually results in another attack. Public speakers and authors are rarely treated as if they are people with feelings. Instead, we can become lightning rods for people who only want to attack.

I share these stories with you because I am sure you can relate to these challenges. Everyone has to endure obstacles like these at one time or another. What similar experiences have you had? Are you living through something like this right now? Yes, we all need to find ways to expel this distress from our brain and body every day, which might include performing an exorcism on these toxic people and getting as many of them out of your life as possible. Otherwise, they will destroy us.

I only wish I knew 50 years ago what I know now about the human brain. I would have made very different choices, which I hope all of you will do by the end of this book.

## MICHAEL'S STORY

Our son Michael was born on Monday, October 25, 1993 at 11:33 am. He was our first child. It was a day and experience I will never forget, and neither will my wife, Lisa.

For the next four years, he was a normal, everyday kind of kid. He was extremely outgoing. From his earliest days in a stroller, Lisa and I would go to the mall and let him interact with other people. As he got older, no one was a stranger to Michael. He laughed, sang, and charmed everyone around him. He was so fast and light on his feet that we used to always make sure he had his favorite bright red Mickey Mouse hat on his head so we could spot him playing with the other kids.

Michael would walk up to people, shake their hand and introduce himself. He warmed the hearts of everyone he met.

Michael also loved books. He loved it when someone read to him. I actually came to dread *Green Eggs and Ham* because it took forever to get through. (It is the *War And Peace* of children's books.) Very quickly, Michael was able to read the book himself. We saw him progress above and beyond his peers. His personality and intelligence amazed us. I remember thinking, "This is a kid we are never going to have to worry about. We are going to be bowled over by what he will accomplish. This kid is amazing!"

When he was three years old, he told his preschool classmates he could read. No one believed him.

So, one day when Lisa went to pick Michael up from preschool, she saw him sitting on a chair in front of all his classmates reading a book. Everyone's eyes were glued on Michael and his reading.

When he was done, one of his skeptical classmates exclaimed, "That was some good readin'!"

That was life with Michael, at least it was for his first four and a half years.

However, in July of 1998, Michael suddenly changed. It was like someone turned off his light switch. He shied away from people. He did not interact with others the way he had in the past. He was much more withdrawn. He did not make eye contact with others. Instead, he would look away when he spoke.

His speech lost its beautifully fluid rhythm. It instead became much more staccato. He stuttered.

He stopped singing altogether.

Instead of gliding on his feet, there was a new stiffness in his walk. His arms stopped swinging with his gait when he moved. Much of his coordination was gone.

Overnight, all of this was happening to Michael—and we had no idea why. That graceful and outgoing kid who Lisa and I enjoyed for the first four and a half years of life had disappeared.

We were terrified. Something terrible was happening to our son, the center of our universe. It was a fate worse than death, as I am sure most parents will understand. We had no idea what to do.

Although we didn't know it at the time, we would never see that four-and-a-half-year-old Michael again. He was gone forever.

Lisa and I took Michael to see psychiatrists and any doctor or specialist we could find to get some answers. We paid whatever fees it took to get our son back, but all we found were dead ends.

Finally, in the summer of 2001, just before Michael was about to start the second grade, we got a diagnosis. We found a psychologist who observed Michael for just a few minutes. The psychologist looked at Lisa and told her that Michael had a condition that had only been classified as a diagnosis since 1993: It was called "Asperger's Syndrome," which she described as being a high-end spectrum form of autism.

We were devastated. The word "autism" just hung in our minds, like we had been hit square in the face with a baseball bat. We knew nothing about this condition, so we educated ourselves.

We later learned that sometimes the symptoms of autism do not present themselves until about the age of three or four years old. The reason for this is because up until that time, children do not realize they are separate from the world. Young children are therefore not self-conscious about how they talk, walk and act. After that age, they see that they are individuals, so they become much more self-conscious, so these various traits rear their heads.

For the next few years, we took Michael to every kind of specialist we could find to get help. Nothing worked. We contacted top psychiatrists who gave us very discouraging news. One psychiatrist told us that was just the way Michael's brain was wired, so there was little we could do. We were told if the issue was chemical, then medications could better address the problem. But because his brain was wired in a certain way, there was not much we could do because you cannot rewire the human brain.

We were then told Michael might need to go to a "special" high school. He might not be "mainstreamed." Worse than that, even though he was extremely intelligent, we were told he might not be able to go to college. These other organizational and social issues might hold him back.

Lisa and I were devastated. So again, we did our own research to find answers.

Later, I had a client who worked for a nuclear PET imaging company. This company could conduct PET scans on cancer survivors to see if there were any cancer cells left in their body. This scan could detect any cancer cells remaining in the body as small as the head of a pin. It was amazing nuclear technology.

My client then told me about her struggles with attention deficit disorder, or ADD. She told me she actually graduated from college without ever having read a book all the way through, which is an amazing feat. She then told me about Dr. Daniel Amen at the Amen Clinics.

She told me that she had gone to the Amen Clinics and had what she called a nuclear SPECT brain scan. She told me how the SPECT scan had helped the doctors better diagnose her

ADD, which allowed them to better treat her condition. She told me this was the best she had ever felt in her life.

I distinctly remembered thinking that maybe, just maybe, this could help Michael. I did not rush into anything. As an attorney, I pride myself on my ability to research anything. If it is out there, I will find it. Whenever I am researching a topic, I become "OCD Man."

For the next few years, I researched Dr. Amen, his clinics, SPECT brain scans, and the human brain itself. I was determined to earn my own informal Ph.D. in neuroscience.

I read all of Dr. Amen's books and listened to all of his lectures. Yes, all of them, which was a lot. I took several online and college-level video courses on neuroscience and neurology from such universities as Carnegie-Mellon University, Harvard School of Medicine, University of Michigan, Princeton, Stanford, Vanderbilt, and Yale School of Medicine, to mention just a few. I also researched several documentaries from the History Channel, PBS, and National Geographic. I read several articles from such publications as *The New England Journal of Medicine*, the *Journal of the American Medical Association*, *National Geographic*, and *Scientific American*. I also read several other books by other reputable sources, as you will see in the bibliography section at the end of the book. I then took this massive amount of information and cross-referenced it with other reliable resources.

I tried to learn everything I could about what the neuroscientists were learning about the human brain. My son's life depended on it. We didn't have ten to twenty years to wait for the medical profession to catch up with the neuroscientists.

I learned that the human brain is the most complicated mechanism in the universe, as far as we know. The human brain contains billions of cells, with trillions of supporting connections, which means there are more connections in the human brain than there are stars in the sky. One piece of brain tissue the size of a grain of sand contains over 100,000 neurons with over a billion connections.[10]

I also learned that if you do not take care of your brain, you will, on average, lose 85,000 brain cells a day. However, if you do take care of your brain, the stem cells living in your brain can grow into about 100,000 new cells every month, and those new cells can grow millions and then billions of additional connections. This is how we can all rewire our brains.[11]

I learned that the brain is the hardest-working organ in our body, and it is an energy glutton. Even though it only makes up about 2% of the body's weight, it uses 20% to 30% of all the calories we consume. It also uses 20% of the oxygen we breathe and about 20% of our blood flow.[12]

I learned the brain actually feels like soft, room temperature butter. It is really fragile.[13]

I learned we can all easily damage our brains with our thoughts. If you expose your brain to a bullying environment, you will be flooding your body with toxic levels of adrenaline and cortisol, and about 20% of those chemicals could be sent to your brain, which is a greatly disproportionate amount compared to the rest of your body mass. Such a flooding of adrenaline and cortisol can literally burn and damage your brain, which can cause a mental disorder.

> **Yes, you can damage your brain with your thoughts.**

(For the purists out there, I will be using the general term of cortisol throughout this book. That term is meant to simplify the various chemicals involved in our body's chemistry, including one of the chief steroid hormones released by our endocrine system, glucocorticoids.)

However, I also learned how exposing the brain to a SAFE environment will do wonders to help repair these damaged neurons. When you expose yourself to a supportive environment, your brain can secrete such positive eustress chemicals such as oxytocin, dopamine, endorphins, and telomerase, to mention a few.

This is why building and maintaining a tolerant or SAFE work environment is not a White thing or a Black thing. It is a human thing. These destructive chemicals don't care about race.

I also learned that we can rewire our brains—literally. This is called "neuroplasticity," which means the brain can rewire itself and change. This is how our brains really do rewire themselves, which is how we can repair those damaged areas.

However, I also learned that chronic distress suppresses the growth of new neurons.[14]

I also learned our brain will literally rewire itself to conform to the environment we subject it to. If the environment we live and work in is toxic and bullying, then the brain will wire itself in a negative way. If we subject it to a positive environment, then it will rewire itself to conform to that environment. Watching a simple 30-minute television program will rewire a part of your brain forever.

> **Neuroscientists call this "social epigenetics."**

Social epigenetics and the distress chemicals produced in war explain why so many of our soldiers return from their deployments with PTSD, and later turn into drug addicts or alcoholics. They are self-medicating the "hot spots" in their brain. Many commit suicide.

I learned that neither Michael nor I were stuck with the current brains we had. We could literally rewire our brains to live better lives.

This is what I learned from the neuroscientists of the world, which was 180 degrees opposite of what we have been told by our $400-an-hour psychiatrists. Our high-priced psychiatrists were wrong about many things, mainly about rewiring the brain. Michael was not predestined to go to a "special" school. He could also likely go onto college one day if he rewired his brain.

I later discovered that once a scientist discovers new medical treatments or diagnostic procedures, it needs to go through a very stringent peer review process, and that can take years.

Unfortunately, using nuclear SPECT brain scans today is considered above the standard of medical care. Treating patients with techniques that go above the standard of medical care can actually endanger that physician's medical license. So, many psychiatrists are not willing to go above the standard of care and face the potential malpractice claims that could follow. Instead, the present standard of care predominates.

I therefore learned that if you want to stay up on the latest and greatest of what is happening in the world of neurology, you go to the neuroscientists, not to the practitioners. This has always been the case, going back to Louis Pasteur, who dared to suggest that physicians were actually making their patients sick by not washing their hands. He was bucking that standard practice of medicine at the time, and it did not go over well.

# MICHAEL'S SCANS

So, in 2006, I took Michael to the Amen Clinic in Reston, Virginia to get his brain scanned.

I chose the Amen Clinic to conduct Michael's scan because they had performed more SPECT brain scans than any other clinic in the world. There was no question where we were going.

I also went to the Amen Clinic because of its holistic approach to medicine. I knew the Amen Clinic's approach was not to just prescribe medications and stop there. The Amen Clinic looks at the whole person, which includes diet, meeting with a nutritionist, exercise, possibly vitamin supplements, and so on.

From all of my research on how the brain works, that made sense.

So, in January 2006, Michael and I flew to the Amen Clinic in Reston to get his brain scanned. Lisa stayed behind in Ohio with our younger son, Nicholas.

Preparing for Michael's scan with the Amen Clinic was intensive. Lisa and I spent well over an hour each talking on the phone to the clinic's intake person. In these interviews, we discussed Michael's background, how he responds to various situations, and so on. It was extremely detailed.

Michael then had to talk to the intake person. Again, this was another hour of intake.

Next, Lisa and I also had to complete a 21-page intake questionnaire on how Michael responded in various situations, which took each of us about an hour to complete.

We also had to complete one with Michael.

Altogether, this was the most thorough intake process I have ever seen, and we had gone through many. Collectively, we spent over six hours completing this process. Clearly, we were supplying the Amen Clinics with a wealth of data they could use to compare to Michael's SPECT scans.

We checked into our hotel on a Sunday night and hit the pool. Michael loved the water and it was a good time to relax, considering what we were there to do.

As I watched him jump in and out of the pool, I could feel my gut clench. I had no idea what we were in for or what we would discover. I didn't know if this whole brain scan thing would work, but we had no options left. I remember thinking, "What can we do to keep him as happy as he is right now?"

Monday morning was our first day at the Amen Clinic. We were taken to a room where Michael was to be injected with the radioactive isotope to make his brain "glow." He was terrified. Michael, understandably so, feared needles. He also wanted to know exactly what they would inject into him and what it would do. Now, this is a 12-year-old boy who is very intelligent and overthinks everything. This is the kid who will actually read the warning signs posted before getting on any thrill ride at an amusement park. So, it was very predictable that Michael would want to know what kind of radiation they would inject into him and what it would do.

The staff was great. They explained to Michael that they were very good with needles and this would only pinch a little. He examined the needle very closely, wrinkled his nose and then gave his OK.

They then explained the radiation he would get was about the same as he would get with a dental x-ray.

"See," I told him. "You've had lots of dental x-rays and you don't look like Charlie Brown."

After about 30 minutes of this, he seemed satisfied. So, they injected him with the isotope. Michael then played the computer game they gave him to stimulate his brain. I could see he was getting frustrated with the game, but that is what it is supposed to do.

When they took Michael into the scanner, I remember them laying him down and the machine moving him into place. Everyone left the room. They showed me where I could wait outside while the exam was being run, but I refused. I wanted to stay in the room with him. I needed to be there.

So, the staff outfitted me with a lead apron and I sat opposite the machine by Michael's feet. The lights dimmed and the exam started. It was all deathly quiet except for the gentle, low pitched humming sound of the scanner. It was comforting and peaceful, which I hoped was a good sign.

I will never forget how helpless he looked going into the machine. This small 12-year-old boy, just as I had been small growing up, would have more to overcome in his life than I could imagine. Would we ever see that exuberant four-year-old Michael again? If not, how was this all going to work? Would he have a normal life? What was waiting for him in his future?

It was all too much to think about. So, I just stared at the machine as it did its work and hoped we would find answers and some viable treatments. I remember thinking this was our last best shot.

When the scan was over, we went to Washington, DC to see as much as we could. This is why Lisa says going on a vacation with us is like going on a school field trip. But Michael and I both love it. It is history. It is real life with real people doing the best they can in impossible situations. It was perfect for this trip.

The next day, we returned to the Amen Clinic for day two. On this day, the clinic took Michael's scans when his brain was calm, which is called a "baseline scan." Again, I sat in the room watching him get his brain scanned, wondering what his future would hold. I knew he would have a much tougher life than most people. The main question was how would he respond to this challenge? Yes, many people have challenges to meet. But when it is your child, it is different. It is worse than if it was happening to you. I thought, "How tough will this little man need to be in the future?"

Once the scan was done, we went back into Washington again for more sightseeing. Yes, another full day of a field trip.

On day three, we returned to the Amen Clinic to meet with the doctor and review Michael's scans, his intake data and discuss his potential treatments.

This is when we first met Dr. Charles Parker, the physician who ran the Reston Amen Clinic at the time. I have always been impressed with Dr. Parker's ability to communicate his opinion in a very clear and calm manner. I was also impressed with his in-depth knowledge and whole-body approach to mental health. Dr. Parker, like the Amen Clinics, doesn't look at just medication to solve a brain functioning problem, he also looks at the metabolic interchanges that occur within the body, which affect your diet, as well as environmental factors, and cognitive behavioral therapies to rewire the brain.

Michael's scans revealed many issues.

Again, the two different types of scans the Amen Clinics take are the activity scans and the blood flow scans.

The activity scans are taken when the patient is at rest, which is called a "baseline scan," and when the patient's brain has been activated or stimulated, which is called a "concentration scan." These two scans are then compared to one another to study the activity levels in our brains.

The blood flow scans look at the level of blood flow going to the brain. Just as with the activity scans, one blood flow scan is taken when the patient is at rest, which is a baseline scan, and the other one is taken when the brain has been activated, which is a concentration scan.

While both types of scans are important, I will focus on our activity concentration scans to show you in a very simple way the results we experienced from our brain health programs, which I will simply call our "concentration scans." This book is long enough without delving any deeper into understanding these various scans. Comparing our concentration scans will prove the points I am making regarding brain health without belaboring the issue.

Another reason I will focus on our concentration scans in these materials is because that is when our brain is in a state of distress, which is when we are at the highest risk of snapping and acting like emotional children.

However, to learn more about both the activity scans and the blood flow scans taken by the Amen Clinics, just go to their website at www.amenclinics.com.

Below is Michael's 2006 concentration SPECT scan. This scan showed his brain was burning way too hot in certain areas and not hot enough in others, as you can see in the following photo:

### Michael's Brain 2006

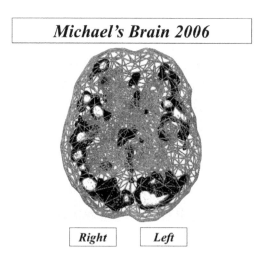

Right     Left

I soon discovered reading these brain scans is pretty easy. In these scans, Michael is lying on his back in the scanner looking up at the ceiling. Therefore, we are looking up through the bottom of his chin at the underside of his brain. His forehead is at the top of the scan and the back of his brain is at the bottom.

Everything in blue is the baseline temperature of Michael's brain. Anything in red is burning about 15% hotter, which means it is more active than other parts of the brain. (In this book, these red areas will show up as black.) However, any areas that show up in white means they are actually burning 20% hotter, which can be a major area of concern, depending on the area affected.

Burning 15% or even 20% hotter can be a real problem. What if you were 15% or 20% taller? Thinner? Or think what would happen if your body temperature rose only 10%? What would happen? You'd be dead. So, firing up your brain to burn 15% or even 20% hotter is a lot.

At the base of his brain, you can see Michael's cerebellum, which controls all of his automatic functions, like breathing, heart rate, and so on. You want this area of the brain to burn as hot as you can get it. Even though the cerebellum only represents about 10% of the brain's volume, it houses 50% of the brain's neurons. It is truly a workhorse for the brain because it is not only involved in our motor coordination, posture, and how we walk, but it also helps us make physical and emotional adjustments, process information, and it governs our organizational skills. People with low levels of cerebellar activity are also often sensitive to touch, light, and noise. Low levels of activity in the cerebellum are often seen in people with autism.

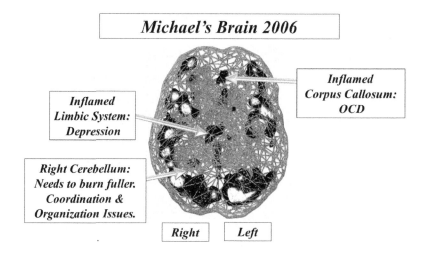

Michael's Brain 2006

Inflamed Corpus Callosum: OCD

Inflamed Limbic System: Depression

Right Cerebellum: Needs to burn fuller. Coordination & Organization Issues.

Right    Left

In this scan, you can see that the left side of his cerebellum was burning red and even white hot, which is very good. However, the right side of his brain was not burning as fully as the other side. Since Michael is left-handed, the right side of his cerebellum is dominant, and it needed to burn much fuller.

This scan of his cerebellum explained why Michael's coordination was so bad. It also helped to explain why his organizational skills were horrendous. Michael had always referred to his collection of school work assignments and notes as "organized chaos." Even though Michael would always complete his homework assignments, he often failed to turn them in for credit the next day. He would either forget or he wasn't able to find his homework assignment thanks to his nest of organized chaos. So, his grades suffered terribly.

At the center of his brain, you will see another red-hot spot. This is Michael's limbic system, which is our emotional center. It is inflamed. Again, when this scan was compared to the mountain of intake data the Amen Clinic collected beforehand, it helped explain why Michael was exhibiting symptoms of depression. However, thanks to the scans, we could also see what part of the brain was causing him problems, which allowed Dr. Parker to better treat these conditions.

At the top of his brain by his forehead, you will see that his corpus callosum was also burning red hot. This red spot indicates that Michael also suffered from a type of obsessive compulsive disorder, or OCD.

To understand OCD, you have to understand what function the corpus callosum fills in the brain. The corpus callosum rests in the center of the brain and it connects the two hemispheres together, which allows them to "talk" with one another. This is why humans are bilateral, which means our thoughts can flow from one side of the brain to the other.

It might be best to think of your corpus callosum like a bridge connecting the two hemispheres. Your thoughts will cross over the bridge to the other side of the brain. However, if your corpus callosum becomes inflamed, as it was in Michael's brain, then these thoughts cannot pass over the bridge. Instead, they will get stuck in this inflammation.

I have always thought of the corpus callosum as the brain's stick shift. You need it to be healthy to easily change gears and shift your thoughts. However, if it gets inflamed, your thoughts will get "stuck." When our thoughts get stuck in the corpus callosum, that is when we "Can't get off it, can't get off it, can't get off it," and so on. So, we obsess.

All of our thoughts are chemical and electrical signals. If these electrical and chemical signals encounter an area of the brain burning too hot or not hot enough, that signal will be disrupted. Depending on what part of the brain is affected, that will determine the mental condition the person will contract.

Sitting right on top of the corpus callosum is the anterior cingulate gyrus. The anterior cingulate gyrus also has many bilateral connections with the two hemispheres of the brain. So, to avoid any confusion, for our discussion, when I am referring to the effects of damaging your corpus callosum in relation to OCD, I will also be referring to the anterior cingulate gyrus.

As a comparison, horses do not have a corpus callosum connecting the two sides of their brain. They are not bilateral. So, if you cover up the left eye of a horse and get to know it, that horse will recognize you as a friend. However, if you uncover the left eye and then cover up the horse's right eye, that horse will not know you. This is because the left side of a horse's brain cannot share what it knows with the right side of the brain, and vice versa. There is no corpus callosum bridge for the message to cross over. So, what is learned in the left hemisphere stays in the left hemisphere.

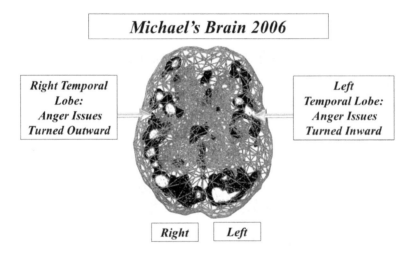

If you look at the two sides of Michael's brain, or his temporal lobes in the graphic above, you will see they are burning way too hot. They are not just burning red, but they are burning white hot.

The right temporal lobe directs many of our anger issues toward the outside world. The left temporal lobe directs many of our anger issues back toward ourselves. This can create a very dangerous situation.

Since Michael's right temporal lobe was burning way too hot, this helped to explain Michael's great rage over being bullied at school, just as I had been bullied as a child. I understood what he was going through all too well.

If you look at his left temporal lobe, you will see it is also burning too hot. This meant many of his anger issues were probably being directed back at himself, which could easily lead to thoughts of suicide.

The massive amount of information we provided Dr. Parker helped immensely in diagnosing Michael's issues and prescribing various treatments. Along with these 2006 scans, Dr. Parker could better understand and more precisely target Michael's condition with better medications and various other therapies and treatments.

Dr. Parker immediately changed the medications Michael was taking and it made a world of difference. Remarkably, we saw an immediate impact on his behavior by simply adjusting his medications to better target Michael's conditions.

When Michael returned to school, his teachers said he was like a whole new kid. He was more alert. He was more interactive. He performed better in class.

Besides these medication changes, we changed his diet. Since 25% of everything you eat is burned by the brain, you are what you eat from a mental standpoint—literally.

Also, your brain has no fat reserves to burn for energy. So, whatever you eat will be burned by your brain immediately, which instantly affects your mood. (Try eating a dozen Krispy Kremes and wash them down with a Mountain Dew—then tell me how you feel.)

We also enrolled Michael in a therapy called the "Interactive Metronome" to develop his cerebellum, which would improve his coordination, his organization skills, and so on. Interactive Metronome therapy has the subject clap their hands and stomp their feet along with the rhythm of the metronome. In the end, Michael's hand and foot coordination improved over 800%. It wasn't easy, but he did it.

Interestingly enough, the clinic where Michael went to receive his therapy for the Interactive Metronome was about two miles from our house . . . and it was in the same building where my wife worked. No doctor or psychiatrist we took Michael to see ever suggested we look into getting this therapy for Michael, even though his organizational and coordination skills were disastrous. The psychiatrists focused solely on his medications, which were not only incorrectly prescribed, but they only made up one part of the treatments and lifestyle changes he needed. These medications did not do anything to rewire or heal his brain. Instead, they suppressed the symptoms of his brain issues. We had to go 400 miles to Virginia to have someone tell us that one therapy Michael desperately needed was in the same building where Lisa works.

When we went to his school for help with his therapies, they provided him with regular balance and coordination therapy. Again, this helped to rewire his cerebellum, which enabled him to run track in junior high and later in high school. We could see Michael was making progress.

So, in 2008, the whole family, Lisa, Michael, Nicholas, and I all went back to the Amen Clinic to see how much progress Michael had made in the last two years.

Below you will see Michael's 2008 scan.

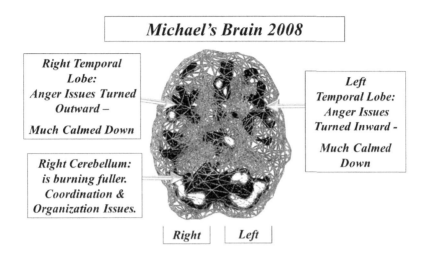

**Michael's Brain 2008**

Right Temporal Lobe: Anger Issues Turned Outward – Much Calmed Down

Left Temporal Lobe: Anger Issues Turned Inward - Much Calmed Down

Right Cerebellum: is burning fuller. Coordination & Organization Issues.

Right     Left

If you look at Michael's cerebellum in this 2008 scan, you will see the right side is greatly improved over his 2006 scan. It is burning much fuller. Actually, both sides of his cerebellum were now burning more evenly. This explains Michael's much improved coordination and his improved ability to organize his thoughts, which enabled him to run track.

Most astonishingly, Michael's temporal lobes were also much improved. The white-hot spots were gone. The temporal lobes were still burning too hot, but we were moving in the right direction.

Michael's diet, therapies and other tactics we adopted were working. His hard work was paying off. His brain was rewiring itself and getting better, so his behaviors were also improving. Much credit must be given to his ability to stick with the programs we put him on. It was difficult, but he did it.

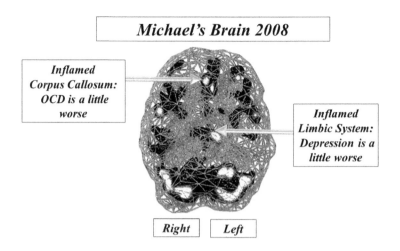

**Michael's Brain 2008**

Inflamed Corpus Callosum: OCD is a little worse

Inflamed Limbic System: Depression is a little worse

Right | Left

However, his corpus callosum had gotten worse, as you can see in the 2008 scan above. That meant his OCD had gotten worse. We could see examples of this coming through in his daily life and how resentful he was over the bullying he had experienced.

This did not mean that Michael did not have good reasons for being bitter over the bullying he had received, but it was only hurting him as he reflected on it. His inflamed corpus callosum was making it much more difficult for him to move on from all of this, and the fact that it was still continuing made it impossible for him to move past it. He was obsessing over it.

Yes, getting our local school system to actually address the bullying and ensuring that it was safe for our kids to go to school was impossible. I hope you can see in this example why tolerance and diversity encompasses so much more than just race. People with brain issues face persecution every day.

If you compare the center of the 2006 and the 2008 scans, which is the limbic system, or our emotional center, the 2008 scan was actually a little worse. In 2008, there was now a white-hot spot showing it was burning 20% hotter than the rest of the brain, which meant his symptoms of depression were getting worse. That was a problem.

You can get a better comparison of Michael's 2006 scan and his 2008 scan from the photo below:

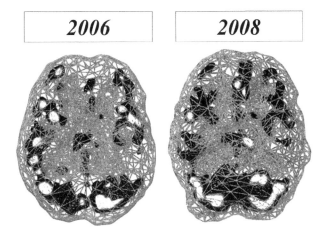

2006      2008

Still, Michael had made great progress. We could see about a 20% improvement in most of his brain functions, which was very encouraging, but he still had a long way to go.

Still, the environment Michael was experiencing daily in our public school system was not just holding him back, but it was making him worse in some ways. Our public school system did little to stop the bullying Michael experienced. When Michael defended himself at school and pushed the bullies to the ground, they stopped picking on him. However, because he physically defended himself, he was punished by the school.

> **When the victim fights back, the victim gets punished.**
> **Yes, life is fair.**

Quite frankly, most of our public schools today care more about our children's test scores than whether they live through the end of the day. Unfortunately, this is also how most employers deal with bullying. They ignore it. It is not safe for most Americans to go to work every day, just like it was not safe for Michael to go to school.

When we found a suicide note Michael had written due to the bullying he was experiencing at school, it was easy to see why his OCD had not improved and his limbic system was becoming more inflamed. When his 2008 intake was compared to his SPECT scans, his depression was getting worse.

Instantly, I thought of my own history. Lisa and I were not going to let this bullying continue, especially once we saw the effects it was having on Michael's brain.

That made our decision easy. We life-flighted Michael out of our public school to a private Catholic high school, Bishop Hartley. Also, since Bishop Hartley had a student population that was a wonderful mix of all races, genders, religions, sexual orientations, and so on, Michael would get to know many types of people as he prepared to go out into the real world. In fact, Michael was a minority at Bishop Hartley. Over 60% of the school was Black.

Paying to send Michael to a private Catholic school was an easy choice, even though we are not Catholic and we are not rich. However, Bishop Hartley had a strict "no bullying" environment, which was religiously enforced. It made little sense to have Michael go through these therapies, eat a certain diet, and take his medications if his brain was continually flooding with adrenaline and cortisol from being bullied. This flooding would only continue to burn his brain and make his conditions worse.

> **It doesn't do any good to take aspirin for a headache when you are still getting beat in the head.**

The cost of tuition was still better than sabotaging his brain health program or planning a funeral.

Michael loved going to Bishop Hartley. The bullying stopped immediately. He actually put on a tie every day to go to school.

In his freshman year, he wanted to run track. This would be good for him socially and also help to improve his brain functions.

This is Michael just before his first high school track meet at The Ohio State University Field House. He was in the ninth grade. Michael chose to be a long-distance runner in high school, running both the 800- and the 1600-meter events.

However, as I watched him run his first 800-meter event at Ohio State, he quickly fell behind the others. After the first 400-meter lap, his body bent. He was running out of gas. He stopped about a third of the way through his second lap. His body just gave out.

If you look at his photo, you can notice his baby face and lack of muscle in his frame. As you can see, he still had a lot of work to do to build his body, which would also further repair his brain. He was not physically ready to run high school track, and I was afraid he would give up. However, this first race only challenged him to fight harder and build up his stamina. For the next four years, Michael trained like an Olympic athlete to run track.

Again, Michael's overwhelming work ethic came into play. His perseverance was amazing to watch. Of course, Michael also continued with his diet, his vitamins, and his therapies.

Michael's transformation through his high school years was remarkable. The muscle mass he put on and how much he transformed his body across his high school years was phenomenal, as you can see in these next photos.

Michael not only graduated from Bishop Hartley High School in 2012, but he also lettered in track, running in both the 800- and 1600-meter events. He also received the "Most Improved Athlete" award for the progress he made in running track across the last four years.

Michael then won an award we had no idea even existed. Every year, the Ohio High School Athletic Association sponsors the "Most Courageous Student Athlete Award." This award is given to the student who overcomes a disability to participate in high school athletics by the Ohio High School Athletic Association. Michael won that award in 2012 for running track at Bishop Hartley.

One of his coaches said he had never seen a kid work as hard and improve as much as Michael. He also told me he wished all of the kids on the track team worked as hard as Michael.

When our youngest son, Nicholas, who is four years younger than Michael, decided that he also wanted to go to Bishop Hartley and he too wanted to run track, the coaches asked the same question: **Does he work as hard as Michael?**

In the fall of 2012, Michael began his studies at The Ohio State University. (Yes, The Ohio State University does more than just play football.)

At Ohio State, Michael became very interested in neuropsychology. Considering his own experiences in this field and the progress he had made with his Asperger's, he decided that was where he wanted his career and life to go.

In his senior year, Michael was also awarded the O'Neill scholarship for academic excellence.

In 2017, Michael graduated with honors from The Ohio State University with a degree in psychology.

(Yes, I almost got arrested hanging off the railing getting these pictures of Michael graduating. However, committing a simple misdemeanor is worth getting these million-dollar shots.)

In May of 2021, Michael graduated with a 3.91 GPA from Roosevelt University in Chicago with his master's in psychology. Michael's goal now is to earn his Ph.D. in neuropsychology and help those diagnosed with autism. (YES, very proud mom and dad here.)

With all of Michael's hard work and accomplishments, in August of 2020, he and I both went back to the Amen Clinics for follow up scans. This is Michael's brain in 2020 as compared to 2006.

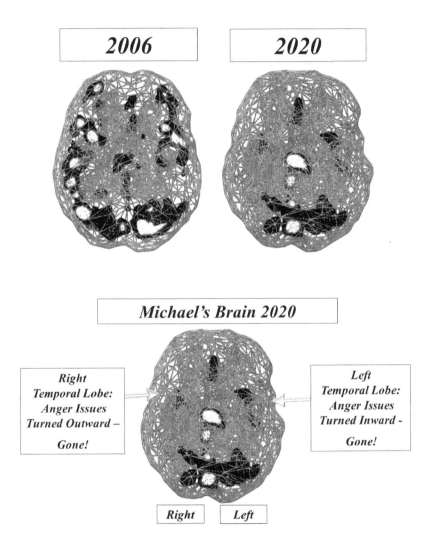

As you can see, the anger issues coming from his temporal lobes are gone completely. He still has a splash of anxiety. His depression still needs attention, as does his OCD.

However, the way Michael has rewired his brain is astonishing, as you can clearly see. Michael had to fight his way back from the lousy cards nature dealt him, but he did it. He is the real hero in this story.

# SCOTT'S SCANS

When we all went to the Amen Clinic for Michael's follow up scan in August 2008, my wife insisted that I get a scan too. I told her that wasn't necessary. She then emphatically told me, "No, you are getting a scan. You are nuts." (Yes, it is important for all of us to have someone in our lives who will tell us what's what.)

As insistent as she was, I had to get the scan. I know who I report to.

The funny thing about being "crazy" is that you rarely know you are crazy—or at least I didn't. It is the same as those people who get hearing aids. They probably needed hearing aids for the last ten years, but they simply adapted their behavior to hide that fact.

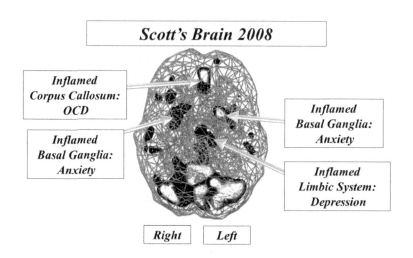

Scott's Concentration Activity Scan: UNDERVIEW

At the base of my brain, you can see my cerebellum, which controls all my automatic functions, like breathing, heart rate, balance, the coordination of my thoughts, and so on. This area is burning very hot in my brain. Actually, it is burning white hot, which is 20% hotter than the rest of my brain. This indicates that I had excellent automatic functions and coordination skills. This also helps to explain my ability to organize my thoughts and projects.

If you look at the center of the brain, the limbic system is inflamed. Since your limbic system is basically your emotional system, this might indicate that I am more emotional and possibly even suffering from the symptoms of depression.

If you next look at my basal ganglia, you can see they are also inflamed. Since the basal ganglia control our level of anxiety, this means my level of apprehension or anxiety is heightened.

And finally, if you look at the top center of my brain scan, which is my forehead, you will see a red stripe with a white-hot spot in the middle. This is my corpus callosum and it is burning really hot. This inflammation of my corpus callosum when compared to my intake data showed that I had OCD.

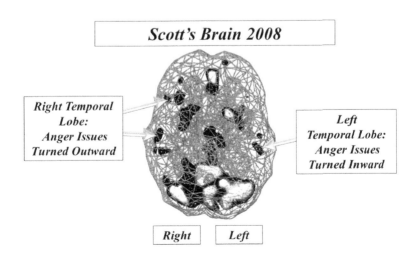

61

If you look at my right temporal lobe, you will see it is damaged. Again, our temporal lobes play a key role in our anger issues.

Since I had severely damaged my right temporal lobe, many of my thoughts of anger were directed towards the outside world. Having been the victim of bullying, I was particularly angered whenever I saw it happening to others. This also explains why I despise the enablers of the world so much. These passive aggressive Retreaters just sit back and watch all of this abuse happen, which makes them just as guilty as the person actually doing the bullying.

If you look at my left temporal lobe, you will see it is also damaged, but not as much as my right side. Since I had damaged my left temporal lobe, some of my thoughts of anger were directed back at myself. This condition can lead to suicide.

### Scott's Brain 2008 With PTSD

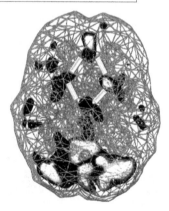

## This Diamond Pattern Is Typical in PTSD

> **When you put this together, anxiety, depression, and OCD all added up to form a diamond pattern typically associated with Post Traumatic Stress Disorder, or PTSD.**

All the information collected from these scans was then compared to the massive amount of intake information collected earlier.

After reviewing all my clinical intake data and my scans, Dr. Parker diagnosed me as having PTSD, as well as other anger issues in my temporal lobes. He also had some specific recommendations for me regarding medications, exercise, diet, and vitamin supplements, to mention a few.

The approach I was given to rewire my brain was much broader and more thorough than just taking a pill. I knew I had to design my own program, just as we had done with Michael. My program consisted of:

1. Get as many jackasses out of my life as possible.
2. Get my physical and fasting blood work.
3. Focus on positive thoughts, friends, and pets.
4. Enjoy my hobbies, such as photography.
5. Engage in a meditation routine.
6. Adopt a new diet lifestyle.
7. Maintain a regimen of vitamin and mineral supplements.
8. Water: Drink half my weight in ounces every day.
9. Get enough sleep.
10. Adopt an aerobic exercise, strength training, and sex program.
11. Get monthly massages.

## SCOTT'S 2020 SCANS

After years of following my program, as I mentioned before, Michael and I returned to the Amen Clinics in 2020 for our follow up scans.

As you can see in my 2020 scans next, my brain was so much better than it was in 2008. By 2020, all of my OCD and temporal lobe anger hotspots were gone. The intake collected by the Amen Clinics corresponded directly with these scans. In those areas, I am back to as normal as I have ever been, probably the first time since I was a very little boy. Yes, I had been cured of many of my brain issues.

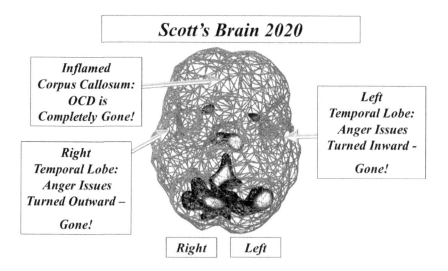

You can compare my two scans from 2008 and 2020 in the next photo.

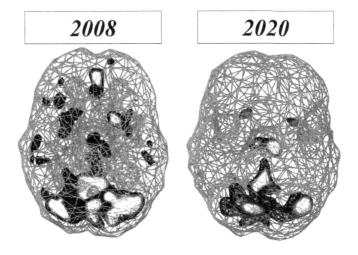

In 2020, we met with Dr. Lillian Somner, a board certified psychiatrist with the Amen Clinics. Once again, the holistic advice she gave us was very helpful. She reviewed our massive intake data and compared them to our 2020 scans. She also reviewed our previous scans to see where we had improved and where we still had more work to do. This is one of the benefits of having your brain benchmarked: You can see what effects aging or other factors might be having on your brain—and what you need to do to fix it.

For instance, the blood flow to the top of my brain, or my parietal lobe, had spots where I was not getting as much blood flow in 2020 as compared to 2008.

Also, my depression was worse in 2020 than it was in 2008, which you can see by my inflamed limbic system in the middle of my brain. Right away, I had a pretty good idea why this was happening to me.

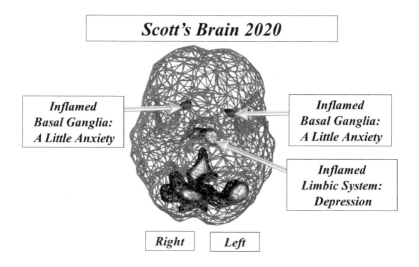

Scott's Brain 2020

Inflamed Basal Ganglia: A Little Anxiety

Inflamed Basal Ganglia: A Little Anxiety

Inflamed Limbic System: Depression

Right    Left

First, we were about six months into COVID when I had these scans. My entire speaking schedule was shot. In the first quarter of 2020, my schedule was packed full of dates to speak across the country. However, by mid-March, all of my speaking dates had been canceled, which was about 80% of my practice. This drop in my business had a tremendous effect on me.

More importantly, I also defied my doctor's advice. Dr. Boris Valdman told me, "No more litigation for you." Litigating my pro bono cases was playing havoc on my blood work, like making my blood sugar levels soar.

Unfortunately for me, I have a great weakness for helping people who are getting screwed over. Being an employment attorney, I will sometimes get calls from people I know whose rights are being trampled on. I will often jump in and help those people who need it on a pro bono basis. I am proud to say I have always gotten a recovery for my clients. The bullies who were abusing my clients have all settled before we ever got to court, although in some instances, it took months or even years to get them to see the light. It took ten years to get the Federal Aviation Administration to see the light regarding a disabled veteran, for example.

Of course, my problem with litigation is that I get way too personally invested. I hate bullies and will never back down. Never.

Still, the toll it takes on my body and my emotional system is too much for me. I simply cannot get involved in such cases again. I find them too upsetting and they destroy my brain, as you can see by my inflamed limbic system in my 2020 scans.

One suggestion Dr. Somner had for me was to start getting hyperbaric oxygen tank treatments, or HBOT. These treatments would give my body increased doses of oxygen that would help rejuvenate my brain even more. She told me she would write a prescription for me to get these treatments and my insurance would probably cover most of the cost. I had a couple of treatment locations in my area.

After investigating HBOTs, I was sold. The research showed that I truly could improve my brain by undergoing these treatments. However, considering the time it would take to go and get these treatments, I decided to buy my own HBOT. It now sits in my basement. We'll see how it goes.

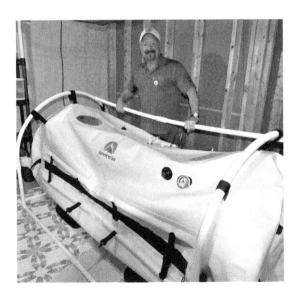

**Scott With His HBOT**

I also started taking some of Dr. Amen's online courses. I found several of these courses to be very helpful and easy to follow, such as the "Change Your Brain: Master's Course," "The 30-Day Happiness Challenge," and the "Brain Fit For Life" course, which is especially geared towards helping employees and teams to become more focused. All of these programs, and many more, can be found at www.amenuniversity.com.

Thank God for doctors like Dr. Daniel Amen, Dr. Lillian Somner, and Dr. Charles Parker.

Had I listened to the traditional standard of care for psychiatry, our brains' health would not have improved. I would be on a handful of psychotropic medications today to suppress the symptoms, if I would still be alive.

I don't even want to think about where my son Michael would be today.

I therefore had to become my own educator and work with a medical team who stayed current with what was happening in the world of mental health and neuroscience.

So, with that, let's next consider the field of neuroscience. We will then look at what Michael and I did to rewire our brains so you can hopefully enjoy those results as well.

# 3

## DISTRESS VS. EUSTRESS

**B**ullies, or as I like to call them, trolls, are everywhere. We all know them. We are related to them and we have all worked with them. We have all felt their negative influences. They send us negative energy, which is why the number one action item on my brain health program was:

> **Get as many jackasses out of my life as possible.**

In my book, *Living The Five Skills of Tolerance*, I described three types of bullies: Barbarian Bullies, Attacker Bullies, and Angel Bullies.

The Barbarian Bully tries to exalt power over others so they can feel superior to them. That is the definition of a pure bully. Nelson Muntz from *The Simpsons* is a perfect example of a Barbarian Bully. They love to bully other people just to boost their own self-esteem, which is usually pretty low. They think if they belittle others, they will move up on the social pecking order. In other words, they think they are taller when they stand on top of more bodies.

The next two bullies are based on our fight-or-flight response.

The passive aggressive Angel Bully, or the Retreater, smiles to your face, and then stabs you in the back when you turn around. They often say they are doing this to be nice. They don't want to hurt your feelings, so they simply lie to your face until you walk away. These are also the enablers of the world. Clearly, this bully is based on our flight response.

As I mentioned in my first book, *Solve Employee Problems Before They Start,* one of the most famous Retreaters of all time was Aunt Bee from *The Andy Griffith Show.* Yes, she smiled a lot and looked like a nice old lady, but whenever there was a conflict, she would sit at the kitchen table with her old biddy friend, Clara, and stab you in the back. In reality, she was one of the worst communicators ever because you would never know there was a conflict until one day it exploded on you.

Retreaters are also the evil enablers of the world because they just stand by and watch the bullies spread their evil and they do nothing. They smile and just watch it all happen.

Retreaters are such a huge problem that the Equal Employment Opportunity Commission said in its "2016 Select Task Force on the Study of Harassment in the Workplace" that "Bystander Intervention" should be included in every organization's harassment training. Bystander Intervention is the single most effective requirement an employer can put into place to stop workplace bullying. Bullying stops 57% of the time within ten seconds whenever a bystander intervenes. This is why the Retreaters are just as bad as the bullies themselves, and they are actually worse than the Attackers. At least with the Attackers you know there is a problem.

The other bully is the little devil, or the Attacker Bully. These are the stereotypical Simon Cowell's of the world who love to "tell it like it is" as they rip your face off. These people will also say, "Hey, I am just being honest" or "I feel very strongly about this" as they attack you to boost their own ego.

Those hypersensitive people who sit right next to you and are offended by the slightest little thing that happens, things that most people would not be upset over at all, can fall into all three of these bullying categories. In order to show how righteous they are to their cause, they either attack you and rip you to pieces or they smile to your face and then later gut you from ear to ear when you are not looking. They routinely think no one should ever offend them and that everyone should bow to their whim. Most people have to walk around them on eggshells, afraid to make even the slightest mistake.

I call these people the "5 Percenters." They are the hypersensitive people who are upset by anything you ever say or do, and every organization has them. For instance, if you gave everyone at your organization a $1,000 bonus, 95% would be thrilled. However, 5% would complain that they had to drive in to get it. Even though I know these hypersensitive people are in the vast minority, it truly weighs on me, especially when weak leaders listen to them for no good reason other than, "No one should ever be offended." (Yes, such reactions strongly indicate there is a mental impairment at work.)

These hypersensitive people are a lot like the zealots during the Inquisition. If you disagree with them, they will torture you until you "see the light."

Such hypersensitive people respond in this manner because they are, in reality, emotional children and intolerant of anyone else's opinion. They do not address and resolve the alleged offense, which is how an emotionally mature person should respond. The sad part is that we usually let them get away with it because, well, no one should ever be offended.

> **All three of these types of bullies prove to everyone it is not safe to be around them.**
>
> **They destroy your trust.**

But more than that, they poison and damage our brains, resulting in a whole basket full of mental disorders. These bullies pose one of the greatest threats to your mental health, if not the worst, as we will discuss later.

That is why every employer must also adopt the following number one action item:

> **Get as many jackasses out of the organization as possible.**

# EMOTIONS ARE CHEMICAL and ELECTRICAL

How our brains work is so obvious that it evades us. Every thought we have is a chemical and electrical reaction. The thoughts we have will dictate the type and amount of chemicals released into our bodies and how our brains will fire electronically. Yes, you really are what you think.

For example, when we eat chocolate, for most of us, it tastes wonderful—maybe too wonderful. We suck on the chocolate and let it melt across our tongues and savor the sweet taste. That is the whole reason we eat chocolate: the taste. (It is not for the nutritional benefits despite whatever the chocolate manufacturers might tell you.)

Contrary to popular belief, you don't have little men running around in your brain delivering messages, despite all the research we have all conducted watching *Looney Tunes* cartoons. Instead, every thought we have is really a chemical and electrical reaction. Chemicals and electrical charges carry these messages throughout our entire body—both positive and negative. So, when we eat chocolate, this is what is *really* happening:

- The chocolate hits our taste buds, which are little chemical sensors spread across our tongue.
- This chemical reaction from the chocolate touching our taste buds "sparks" an electrical charge.
- This message is then transferred onto our emotional system, which says, "Wow! This is really good! Is there any more?"
- The stimulus also goes to the frontal lobes, which registers with us by saying, "I recognize this. This is chocolate."

What is actually happening in our brains is that we have just gotten a little shot of cortisol, a little shot of adrenaline, and a nice flow of other various chemicals that make us feel good. This chemical balance in our bodies is very comforting, which is where we get the term "comfort food."

The same chemical reaction occurs when we engage in our favorite hobbies or we work with positive people. This helps put us in the "Flow" of what we are doing, which means we have a nice balance of adrenaline and cortisol in our brain, and a nice flow of dopamine, endorphins, and other energizing chemicals, that we call "eustress." If we are working with someone we like, we will even release a little flow of oxytocin, which is another very pleasing and comforting chemical in our brain that gives us the feeling of happiness or pleasure. When we experience such a positive chemical cocktail in our bodies, we become extremely productive and even lose ourselves in our work. Our brain actually calms down and uses much less energy when we are in this positive state of concentration. Our heart rate slows down, our hands warm, our muscles relax and our breathing becomes deeper. The day shoots by and we are energized by what we did all day. Such an environment is not only very productive, but it is also very healthy for us.

Therefore, maintaining a positive attitude and supportive relationships in our lives is beneficial not only from a production standpoint, but also for our overall physical and mental health—both short and long-term. Neuroscience has shown us that living and working in such a positive environment will result in us having a balanced level of chemicals released in our systems, much like the nice flow of a lazy river, and many chemicals that promote our overall health. This is why we describe being in such a mental state as being in the Flow, which I will address in more detail later.

But maintaining negative attitudes and toxic relationships will cause a flood of adrenaline and cortisol to rush throughout our systems like a raging typhoon, which is distress. Flooding our bodies with massive amounts of adrenaline and cortisol will overwhelm many of the other chemicals that promote our overall health, which will inevitably weaken our immune systems, greatly harm our ability to remember even the simplest of things and, over time, will slowly burn our brains and poison our bodies.

Every time you have angry or upsetting thoughts, your brain releases chemicals that make your body feel bad and activates your emotional system. We have all experienced this phenomenon when we get upset or angry. Our muscles tense, our heart beats faster, our palms sweat and we might even feel a little dizzy. Our body reacts to every negative thought we have and puts us into some degree of fight-or-flight, which floods our bodies with adrenaline and cortisol.

Dr. Mark George, M.D., from the National Institute of Mental Health, conducted a study that showed the effects negative thoughts have on our deep limbic systems, or our emotional brain. Dr. George found that when his subjects were thinking happy thoughts, their emotional system cooled down. However, when they were thinking sad thoughts, the activity in their emotional system greatly increased. This study demonstrated that every time you have positive thoughts, your brain releases chemicals that make your body feel good and cool you down.

Everyone has distress. However, unless we do a better job limiting distress, which is the massive amounts of adrenaline and cortisol surging through our brains and bodies every day, and then clearing this cortisol out of our systems on a daily basis, we will be looking at possibly contracting several serious conditions, one of which could be Alzheimer's.[16]

> **Yes, bullies can give you Alzheimer's.**

Actually, researchers have discovered that . . .

> **Suffering from depression and having rampant negative thoughts doubles the risk of Alzheimer's.**[17]

Therefore, unless we change our behaviors and lifestyles, Alzheimer's is expected to triple in the next 25 years. In fact, Alzheimer's begins to form in the brain 30 to 50 years before we become symptomatic.[18]

Besides drastically increasing our susceptibility to Alzheimer's, researchers have also discovered that greatly heightened levels of cortisol damages, shrinks, and kills the neurons in our hippocampus, which is our short-term memory transmitter, by as much as 14%.[19]

Therefore, taking proper care of your brain can actually prevent or greatly delay the onset of Alzheimer's.

Think of it this way: Is gasoline good for your car? Yes, of course. If you don't have gasoline for your car, it won't run. But what if you filled your tank with gas, and then covered the outside of your car, and the interior, with gasoline? That is how constantly flooding your body with adrenaline and cortisol should be viewed. It becomes toxic at such chronically high levels.

## TYPES OF STRESS: DISTRESS vs. EUSTRESS

When most people hear the term "stress," they usually think of distress. Distress is the negative and destructive form of stress because it floods our system with high levels of adrenaline and cortisol. So, when I say distress, you should think "massive amounts of adrenaline and cortisol." That is why you hear so many people say that "stress kills." What they really mean to say is that distress kills, because at continuously high levels, it is toxic to the human brain and body.

Eustress, on the other hand, is a positive and productive form of stress that occurs when we become energized or exhilarated, when we associate ourselves with positive people, when we engage in activities that have meaning for us, or we feel we are playing an important role in accomplishing some higher goal. Eustress releases a much more positive and healthy flow of chemicals throughout our entire body so we feel energized and invigorated by the challenge.

We experience eustress when we engage in hobbies, such as gardening, hiking, or running, for example. We also experience eustress when we work with very supportive people, or when we throw ourselves into a task we enjoy and find challenging. Experiencing eustress is how we get into the Flow and become very productive.

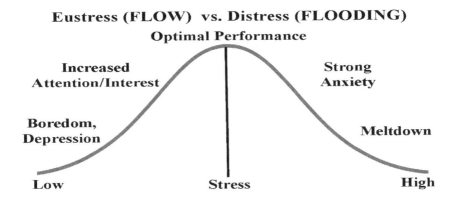

## Eustress (FLOW) vs. Distress (FLOODING)

Optimal Performance

Increased Attention/Interest

Strong Anxiety

Boredom, Depression

Meltdown

Low        Stress        High

**THE U-EFFECT AND FLOW: THE PSYCHOLOGY OF OPTIMAL PERFORMANCE**

As you can see, the primary difference between eustress and distress is the type and balance of the chemicals released in our bodies. Therefore, one of the primary factors that will determine if we flood or Flow is the amount of adrenaline and cortisol our bodies produce.

When we are in a good mood and when we get into the Flow of what we are doing, we have a mild to a moderate level of adrenaline and cortisol flowing throughout our bodies. However, if our stress level continues to climb after we have reached an optimal point where we can learn and perform at our best, such as when we experience overwhelming fear, then our systems overload. The same adrenaline and cortisol chemicals that helped put us into the Flow actually work against us when we overload and flood our bodies with them.

As we continue to experience more distress, our body secretes more adrenaline and more cortisol. Eventually, our body and brain begin to flood and overload with these chemicals. Our emotions slide into a state of panic, which can easily turn into an emotional hijacking. Learning, the ability to reason, and to solve problems, and to control our emotions all drop off remarkably.[20]

Mihaly Csikszentmihalyi, a psychology professor at the University of Chicago who has studied human enjoyment since 1963, developed the theory of Flow. The question he posed to himself was simple:

> **What makes some experiences enjoyable ... and other experiences not?**

Why can some people go out into their yard and garden for hours under the hot sun, only to feel invigorated when they are done? However, these same people will then go into work, use a third of the energy they spend on their hobbies and feel exhausted at the end of their shift. What is the difference?

It is the difference between distress and eustress—or between flooding and Flow.

In searching for this answer, Csikszentmihalyi interviewed many people who enjoyed various kinds of activities. He discovered that certain basic factors were common to all of their experiences. In researching the state of Flow, Csikszentmihalyi interviewed several painters to understand the state of mind they were in when they felt they were the most productive. In his book, *The Evolving Self,* Csikszentmihalyi said that when painters got into the Flow of their work, they couldn't tear themselves away from it. They got immediate feedback on their work when they met the challenge of the next stroke of the brush. They actually forgot all about being hungry, their social obligations, and fatigue. Time lost all meaning. The challenge of changing and developing the painting stimulated these artists.

However, once the painting stopped being a challenge, the fascination and the Flow stopped.

Csikszentmihalyi called this state of mind "Flow" because that was how so many of his interviewees described it. They said this was when they enjoyed their work the most and they were challenged at the same time. They entered this state of mind they called Flow, just as if they were being carried away by a current and everything moved smoothly without effort.

Most of us have experienced that particular state of mind at one time or another. Whenever we are doing something we enjoy that also challenges us, we can experience Flow. Our activity becomes a very rewarding exercise, much like it did when we played as children. Engaging in the activity was the reward.

As adults, some of us play games like poker or chess, engage in sports, work in the yard or in our gardens, play musical instruments, read books, hike, or engage in dozens of other activities. While some would hate planting flowers, other people live for it. We all have different things we like to do that will put us into that magical emotional and mental state of Flow. The common theme here is that we enjoy these activities *and* they challenge us.

Becoming totally absorbed by the task and focusing on its outcome is key. That is what we call "fun."

Therefore, we humans do not enter a state of Flow filled with eustress when we are relaxing. Instead, it occurs when we are actively engaged in a difficult task, one that challenges our mental and physical abilities and takes us away from those anxieties that consume us so much of the time.

Csikszentmihalyi says that whenever we enter this state of Flow, that is as close as we can get to what we call "happiness."

## GETTING INTO THE "FLOW" WITH EUSTRESS

So, how do we get into the Flow of our work? How can we get those same eustress chemicals flowing throughout our body at work that we experience when we engage in our favorite hobbies, like gardening, hunting, hiking, and so on? How do we make our jobs as interesting as our hobbies?

First, you must look for the meaning in your work. If you are just killing time until 5:00 p.m., you will not get into the Flow of what you are doing. You need to discover what is important and satisfying about your job. If your job does not have any meaning for you, it will be filled with distress.

For instance, I once went to a seminar on motivating employees and one speaker was the CEO of a pet yard service. This company hires employees to go to other people's homes and pick up all their dog poop. Now, if you ever thought you should have studied harder in school, it was probably the day you were hired as a human "pooper-scooper."

As I listened to the CEO talk about his company and his employees, they did not look at their jobs as human "crap magnets." Instead, these employees understood who they were serving.

Most of this company's clients were older people and people who were visually impaired. These people simply could not go out and pick up their own yards. For most of their clients, the primary relationship they had in this world was with their dog. Many of these older people could go days on end without having any other contact with any living thing. If it wasn't for the service provided by this organization, these clients could not keep these pets, which means they would have no real contact with any other living thing day after day after day.

As for this company's visually impaired clients, their seeing-eye dogs were the only way they could maintain their independence. If they could not keep these dogs, they would lose many of the everyday freedoms many of us take for granted.

Therefore, these employees were not just picking up yards. They were providing their clients with a second chance at life.

The company itself made sure they were in close contact with their employees. The employees were constantly getting both positive feedback and coaching. The employees were valued.

The company also created a SAFE environment. It was not just safe for their fingers and toes, but it was SAFE for them to be different. That meant it was safe to be White, Black, female, gay, Democrat, Republican and so on. It was a truly inclusive culture.

It was also SAFE to disagree with each other. Different people have different opinions on many things, and that is OK. It was actually a serious offense to attack someone else because they had an opinion different from yours, or to be passive aggressive and stab a co-worker or subordinate in the back for disagreeing with you.

It was truly a tolerant and SAFE culture.

A few years ago, a good friend gave me a book. It was called, *The Simple Truths of Service: Inspired by Johnny the Bagger* by Ken Blanchard and Barbara Glanz.

In this true story, a 19-year-old man with Down Syndrome was hired as a bagger at a large grocery store. To put a little extra meaning into his customers' day, as well as his own, he found and printed up a "thought for the day" for all the customers who came through his line. Johnny would first find a thought or a quote from someone that he liked and then print off copies of this message onto pieces of paper. When he bagged a customer's groceries the next day, he would put the small piece of paper with his thought for the day into his customer's bag.

At first, people would read his thought for the day, smile, and then go about their business. However, after a while, customers got in line wherever Johnny was bagging groceries to get his thought for the day. Customers came into the grocery store more often to buy things just to get Johnny's thought for the day. Eventually, few customers wanted to go into anyone else's line. They wanted to see Johnny's "thought for the day" and they would wait in line to get it, even though other check-out lanes had no one waiting. Johnny's "thought for the day" changed the culture of the entire grocery store.

Johnny brought meaning to the customers, his fellow employees, and himself. He brought a state of Flow to his own work, which also gave him a daily dose of healing eustress chemicals that would enrich his life. Johnny's work days would just fly by.

It is important to note that the grocery store created a good environment for its employees, but Johnny enriched his own life by enriching the lives of others. There is nothing fuzzy or feel good about this story. Johnny, all on his own, redesigned his job to where he found it fulfilling because it filled his life with Flow.

In the town where I live, Reynoldsburg, Ohio, we recently got a new Little Caesar's Pizza shop. (We were all very excited over this.) To bring in business, Little Caesar's hired a young man to stand out in front of the shop with a sign that said: "$5 Pizzas!"

Now, like many jobs we see people doing every day, standing out on the street corner with a Little Caesar's Pizza sign is not the most exciting job in the world, and to many people, it might be a little embarrassing. You are given a bright orange sign, you stand out on the street corner, and you show the sign to people driving home from work. Most would simply laugh at you and say, "That poor schmo. What a lousy job."

However, our Little Caesar's Pizza guy put his personality into his job. He enriched it. Rather than just standing on the street corner holding his sign looking like an idiot, he put in the ear buds for his iPod, and then spent the next few hours dancing, twirling his sign, and entertaining everyone who drove by him. He not only became a fixture on the streets of Reynoldsburg, but he was actually featured on CNN.

In these jobs, jobs most of us would never want to do, these people have found very simple ways to make the job their own. They have discovered a personal meaning in what they were doing, or they were building such strong relationships with their peers that they will actually rush into battle in their underwear.

They have discovered the healing and energizing power Flow.

Giving meaning to what we do energizes us because it puts more eustress chemicals into our bodies—and that is **your** responsibility. It is your life. It is your job. If your job or your life does not have meaning, then give it meaning, just like these people did in these examples.

We already do this when we find meaningful ways to exercise.

For instance, what if I told you we would all exercise and run as fast as we can in a square in 60-foot intervals? We would all run for 60 feet, then make a hard left and run another 60 feet, then make another sharp left turn and run again, and then another hard left turn and run some more? And what if I told you we would take a short break, and then do it all over again for the next hour? How would you feel about that? We all would hate it!

Why does that exercise program sound so terrible? **BECAUSE IT HAS NO MEANING!** We are simply running in a square with no real goal and with no true purpose. Where is the intrinsic reward? Where is the motivation? Where is the eustress?

But what if I told you we would play kickball for the next hour? Doesn't that sound better? Most of us would jump at the chance. (Now you know why kickball leagues have been popping up all over the country.)

The point I am making here should be clear:

In anything you do, there is a way to put your mark on it and make it have meaning for you. It might be the way you perform the job. It might be the relationships you build with the people who surround you every day. It might even be as simple as the way you view your job and why it is important.

Regardless of how you find meaning, it is vital that you do. Otherwise, your job will slowly choke the life out of you just as if you were lunch for a boa constrictor.

Unfortunately, too many people will try to destroy your Flow and the eustress chemicals you need to survive, and it has happened to me many times. It is one of the great causes of our mental disorders.

One of my most devastating professional disappointments happened back in 2008. For 13 years, I delivered my "What The HECK Happened? Employment Law Update" presentation at a human resource conference in Ohio. Once a year, I went to this conference to see many friends, refill my soul, and to build relationships with others. The discussions I had with these people throughout the year continued to give me several hours of eustress chemicals. It was a religious experience for me, I thrived on it, and since I had just been diagnosed with PTSD, I needed it more now than ever.

I never charged the conference a fee for my program. Money was not a motivator at all, and I turned down every offer of compensation. I wanted it to be a pure experience. I even turned down paid bookings with other conferences so I could be at this one every year.

In fact, to make the session more fun, I always took a couple of hundred t-shirts with me to give away to the attendees. I spent weeks designing and personalizing all of these shirts myself with graphic transfers of Underdog, Troll Dolls, Mark Twain, and others who tied into my program. My presentation was more like a big party than an employment law update and I loved it, and so did the attendees.

Every year, it was one of the top-rated programs at the conference, if not the number-one program. This session was so popular that the conference leaders expanded the length of the program from 60 to 90 minutes. The conference leaders also changed it from being a breakout session to a general session so everyone could attend. Going to this annual conference and renewing my relationships was going to be a big part of my brain health program. With my PTSD diagnosis, I knew I would need these eustress chemicals more than ever before in my life. The key for me was that I was helping hundreds of people all at once by doing something I was good at and I loved.

In September 2008, one month after my diagnosis, I once again presented "What The HECK Happened? Employment Law Update" at the conference as a general session, and I jumped in with both feet. It was the highest-rated program at the conference and I spent all my spare time with old friends and making new ones. I could feel the eustress chemicals filling my brain. It was exactly the medicine I needed.

However, in November 2008, three months after I got my PTSD diagnosis and two months after the conference, one of the conference leaders told me that five or six attendees had complained that I was back presenting at the conference every year. As a result, I would not be asked to speak at the next conference. After 13 years, I was out.

Now, I had over 600 people attend my session, and it was the highest-rated session at the conference that year. I could not understand how I could be dropped after 13 years of volunteering, not because of the 5 Percenters, but because the "1 Percenters" complained.

I was devastated.

So, I spoke with my wife and several of my human resource friends. They agreed that this did not make any sense at all. Why would the conference leadership listen to five or six people out of 600?

So, I wrote a letter to the entire board. I explained that I had presented at this conference free of charge for 13 years and that I did not think it was fair to listen to five or six of the attendees. Instead, they should listen to what the other 594 people thought. I even suggested the board conduct a Survey Monkey questionnaire to see what the attendees really wanted to see at the conference. I ran this letter by several former conference chair people and former board members to make sure I was not coming off as offensive or unreasonable. Everyone I asked to proofread the letter said it was very fair and reasonable. I still have the letter to this day. I often reread it with fresh eyes just to make sure I was not being offensive, second guessing my actions.

So, I sent the letter. However, it ended my relationship with the conference forever.

The truth of the matter was that the conference official had lied to me. The conference leadership only wanted to take a break for one year. Five or six people had not complained. That was a lie.

When I later asked why the conference official lied to me, why she just didn't tell me the truth, I was told, "She didn't want to hurt your feelings. So, she lied."

Yes, the conference leadership did not have any trouble with the fact that I was lied to, but because I had written this letter asking them to reconsider this decision based on that lie, I had committed a mortal sin.

If I had known the truth, I would have never sent that letter asking the board to reconsider their decision. Taking a break for a year makes sense. Canceling me because 1% of the attendees complained did not.

I was also told that the conference board thought I was becoming too popular. They felt it was becoming the "Scott Warrick Show," so they wanted to put an end to that.

In December 2008, I started getting emails from my clients asking me about the 2009 conference as they prepared their budgets for that next year. Since early bird registrations come out long before the speakers are announced, I didn't want my clients to sign up thinking that I was going to be presenting. So, I sent out an email to those people on my distribution list telling them that I was not going to be back in 2009. This upset the conference officials even more. However, rather than discussing with me why I sent the email to my clients, I was ostracized, and it was always behind my back.

Many of the conference officials started telling everyone throughout their network that I was too difficult to work with and that my ego was in the way. One human resource chapter president told me that I would never be welcome at his chapter, and I didn't even know this person.

For years after that, I would make submissions to present at the conference, but my submissions were just tossed to the side. They were not even considered.

At a time when I was battling to overcome my PTSD, as well as trying to help Michael repair his brain, these attacks had a tremendously damaging effect on me and my family—and they went on for years.

In the end, my relationship with that conference, and the eustress chemicals I got from it, were gone forever.

So, what is the moral of this story? That is life, isn't it? For whatever reason, people will lie to you and try to destroy the good things in your life, often because of pure ego.

I am sure you have had similar experiences. What were they? What effect did they have on you physically? Are they happening to you right now? Remember: If chronic distress is causing you to experience physical issues, your brain is already being affected.

However, if we want to survive, we all need to see if we can eliminate these trolls from our lives. We will also need to find other sources of eustress fulfillment because our body and brain health demand it.

However, THIS time, I had a much better idea how to handle this distress, which is what I want for you once you have finished this book.

I tried volunteering to present for other groups to help them with their programming. I actually found this to be a lot harder than you would think. Actually, many groups simply did not believe that I really just wanted to help. One group wanted to charge me to present to their people, which is not something I do. Too many people suspected that I had an ulterior motive since they couldn't grasp the fact that I might want to help them for the sole reason that altruism has strong healing powers. It is such a foreign concept in our society that anyone would want to help others because it is good for them and not be motivated by money.

Now you know why I do so many free podcasts. When someone won't let you play in their stadium, you build your own. The eustress chemicals and Flow that I get from helping other people helps to heal me.

You also now know why I turned to writing my books. I feel fulfilled when I tackle a new book, and I only write about topics that are driving my passion. The greatest reward that I could ever get is to hear that someone's life was made better by reading one of my books, watching one of my videos, or coming to one of my sessions. The eustress chemicals it gives me are better than gold.

I took on more pro bono cases. My skill set as an employment attorney can be used to help those people who need it when they are being bullied, and there is plenty of opportunity out there. Many of these cases I was able to resolve very quickly, while others almost destroyed me. The lies and deceit you see amongst lawyers and their sexually harassing clients literally made me sick. Yes, you might get rich defending perverts, but you are still going to burn in hell—probably in the special section they have reserved for litigators.

However, whenever I get attacked these days, I will look through a file I keep with tokens and comments from people who appreciate what I do and who I have helped over the years.

I will also look up at my bookcase where two empty bottles of wine now sit. They are from an old friend who I helped when she was being bullied by her employer and forced out of her job. That was the "fee" she paid me, and it still fills me with Flow and eustress chemicals.

When I first started my full-time private practice over 20 years ago, my wife got me a framed poster that quotes Dante Alighieri's *Inferno*. It reads:

> "The hottest places in hell are reserved for those who, in times of great moral crisis, maintain their neutrality."

I try to live up to that standard every day. It gives me purpose and my life greater meaning. And inside the frame of that poster rests a lottery ticket and a fresh $1 bill. These are gifts from people who heard my tolerance presentation or read my *Living The Five Skills of Tolerance* book and wanted to thank me.

I smile every time I look at these gifts.

This story applies to all of us. Employees often look to their employer to give their jobs meaning and importance, only to have someone in that organization turn on them, often due to pure ego. Yes, that will happen to you, and it has happened to me.

However, as any mature adult knows, it is **your** life. You are responsible for you. You need to get meaning from the job you do and keep items around you that remind you of who you are and the good you are doing. If you feel that is impossible, then you need to find another job.

# GOOD EUSTRESS CHEMICALS

As we discussed, some of the most positive and healthy chemicals that our brains produce are generated when we experience eustress. Neuroscientists have identified several pleasure-inducing neurotransmitters generated when we interact with other positive people.

Yes, my goal is to increase your stress levels—your eustress levels, that is.

## Oxytocin

When we engage in positive interactions with others, such as when we help a loved one or when we engage in activities with supportive people, our brains will often give us a nice "shot" of oxytocin, which generates a sense of satisfying relaxation in us. That is why oxytocin is sometimes called the "hugging drug."

Oxytocin causes our brains and our bodies to experience many healthy changes. As the oxytocin flows throughout our brain, we grow more and more relaxed. Our blood pressure drops. Oxytocin also acts as a stress hormone "down-regulator," so our cortisol levels drop. In this relaxed state, our metabolism can revert into a more "restorative" mode where our energy can then be used for storing nutrients, growth, and healing our bodies. Our wounds will then heal faster. Our threshold for experiencing pain also rises, so we are less sensitive to discomforts.

Unfortunately, oxytocin has a short life span in the brain. It can dissipate in just a matter of minutes. But having positive long-term relationships in our lives can offer us a relatively steady source of oxytocin, which will work wonders in maintaining a healthy body while dissipating the harmful effects of flooding our systems with cortisol.

Kerstin Uvnäs-Moberg, a Swedish neuroendocrinologist, has studied the effects of oxytocin in the human brain extensively. Dr. Uvnäs-Moberg states that whenever we engage in affectionate contact with someone we care for, which includes sex, we get a nice flow of oxytocin. Since the neural circuitry for many of our oxytocin receptors intersect with many neurons that run through our emotional system, the emotions we experience for others can become very strong and very motivating.

Uvnäs-Moberg found that if we have repeated encounters with people with whom we have close social bonds, our bodies will condition themselves to release oxytocin by merely being in the other person's presence or just thinking about them. Therefore, humans can actually prime each other with the good feelings that oxytocin provides. Such revelations support allowing employees to place their personal items and the photos of their loved ones in their work areas. When we see these familiar faces and personal mementos, thanks to such hormones and neurotransmitters as oxytocin, we really do physically connect with these people even though they are not present. Yes, we humans literally do become physically connected with others.

This chemical connection with others also explains why we experience such physical and mental anguish over losing a loved one, including our beloved pets. When we can no longer see this person, the chemical connection we have established is physically broken. The inability to make this connection causes us humans to experience actual physical pain.

## Dopamine

The discovery of dopamine in the 1990s has been one of the most interesting revelations in the world of neuroscience. Lately, dopamine has received a great deal of press, so it is now one of the best-known neurotransmitters.

The brain uses dopamine in a variety of ways. Since dopamine is most heavily concentrated in the pleasure systems of the brain, it plays a crucial role in our level of motivation and our ability to experience pleasure. When our brains continue to release dopamine, we experience prolonged feelings of enjoyment. Dopamine reinforces those activities we engage in that make us feel good, such as when we eat food we like, have sex, and so on.

That is why dopamine is commonly called the "motivation drug."

Additionally, it is because of our dopamine receptors that we become addicted to sugar and fats. When we eat sugar and fats, our dopamine receptors fire with excitement. They overload with dopamine—and these receptors want more. They crave to repeat that first unique sugar or fat "high," which is hard to do. So, to reach the heightened pleasure of that first high, we eat more and more and more. That is why we humans really do become addicted to sugar and fats the same as we do with heroin.

However, describing dopamine as simply the "reward chemical" is far too simplistic an explanation. Since dopamine controls the flow of information from our frontal lobes to other parts of the brain, when dopamine levels drop too far, neurological functions such as memory, attention span, and problem solving all decline. Therefore, neuroscientists believe that one cause of attention deficit disorder is related to low dopamine levels in the brain. This is why dopamine stimulants sometimes work in correcting this problem.

Dopamine also affects the way the brain controls our movements. If someone has too few dopamine receptors in certain parts of their brain, that person can develop Parkinson's disease.[21]

However, too much dopamine in the brain has been linked to schizophrenia. In addition, addictive disorders related to an overloading of dopamine range from alcoholism to drug abuse to compulsive gambling.

Interestingly, dopamine is actually a rare commodity in the brain. Scarcely more than .03% of the neurons in the brain can produce dopamine, but the impact it has on our mental and physical health is tremendous.

Even with all that we have discovered in recent years, neuroscientists are only now understanding the key roles dopamine plays in our brain.

## Serotonin

Serotonin is an important neurotransmitter thought to induce pleasure in humans. (Actually, the precursor to serotonin is the amino acid L-tryptophan. Once it enters the brain, L-tryptophan is converted into serotonin.) Low levels of serotonin are thought to result in depression, anger, sleep disorders, worrying, moodiness, emotional rigidity, irritability, sexual disorders, and even vomiting. The average adult human maintains only about five to ten milligrams of serotonin, 90% of which reside in the intestines. The remainder can be found in our blood platelets and in the brain.[22]

Serotonin was first isolated and identified in 1948 by Maurice Rapport, Arda Green, and Irvine Page of the Cleveland Clinic as a powerful vasoconstrictor in blood serum. Later, it was associated with the central nervous system.

Today, serotonin is seen as a "wonder drug." In our brains, it acts as the neurotransmitter that allows our body to function in many ways, such as controlling appetite, sleep, memory and learning, temperature regulation, mood, behavior, cardiovascular function, muscle contraction, endocrine regulation, and even depression. It is widely believed that no other physiological substance regulates as many of our bodily functions as serotonin.

Serotonin is manufactured in the human body by converting the essential amino acid L-tryptophan, which is found in foods such as bananas, pineapples, plums, turkey, and milk.

Low levels of serotonin are believed to cause mild to severe depression, which can lead to other psychological disorders such as anxiety, apathy, fear, feelings of worthlessness, insomnia, and fatigue.

However, if the symptoms of depression are mild enough, they can sometimes be managed without using any prescribed medications. The most effective way of raising serotonin levels in your body is with exercise. Studies have shown that our serotonin levels rise with increased physical activity. This heightened level of serotonin production remains high for many days after exercising. Exercising is therefore the safest way to increase serotonin levels.

Serotonin levels can also be controlled through the diet. A diet deficient in omega-3 fatty acids has been shown to lower brain levels of serotonin, which often results in depression. Complex carbohydrates raise the level of L-tryptophan in the body, and thus serotonin in the brain, resulting in calmer moods.

To maintain adequate levels of serotonin in your body, take your daily requirements of vitamin C, since vitamin C is needed to convert L-tryptophan into serotonin.

Recent discoveries have also revealed that serotonin is key in modulating our sense of fairness. In one study, researchers depleted the serotonin levels in their subjects. The researchers then asked the subjects to participate in an "Ultimatum Game." In this game, a proposal is made to the subject to unevenly split a sum of money. If the subject accepts, both parties get paid. However, if the proposition is rejected, both parties walk away with nothing.

Typically, the subjects rejected the lowball offers they were made, which offered them only 20% to 30% of the total sum.

When the subjects were made offers of a 60% to 40% split or something similar, these offers were accepted.

However, when those subjects' level of serotonin was depleted, they turned down proposals that offered them an amount as high as 80% of the total. Researchers discovered that even though the subjects' moods did not change, their behavior, or their sense of "fairness," was severely skewed when they ran short of serotonin. When these subjects' serotonin levels were depleted, they became very unreasonable and wanted "it all for themselves."[23]

## Endorphins

Another vital neurotransmitter we humans rely heavily upon are endorphins. However, there are at least 20 types of endorphins in humans.[24] Endorphins, which are naturally-occurring opiates, have the same pleasure inducing feelings as heroin. Actually, the endorphins produced by our bodies are stronger than the morphine we inject our soldiers with when they are wounded.

Most people associate endorphins with stress and pain, which are the two most common factors leading to the release of this neurotransmitter. When our bodies have a nice flow of endorphins, we not only feel less pain, but this neurotransmitter greatly lessens the negative effects we feel from distress. Endorphins are also partly responsible for the famous "runner's high" that athletes experience with prolonged exercise.

Endorphins interact with the opiate receptors in the brain to reduce our awareness of pain, which acts in a similar manner to such drugs as morphine, codeine and heroin. However, unlike these other drugs, activating your opiate receptors with endorphins does not lead to any addiction or dependence.[25]

However, looking at endorphins as merely pain killers is selling these neurotransmitters way short. Secreting endorphins also gives us feelings of euphoria, regulates our appetite, releases sex hormones, and enhances our immune system.

The endorphins released throughout the brain vary from person to person. Two people who exercise at the same level or suffer the same pain will not necessarily produce the same level of endorphins. Also, certain foods, such as chili peppers, can also increase the level of endorphins in our bodies. In addition, one reason we crave chocolate when we become distressed is due to the endorphins released when we eat this tasty treat. (This was the reason I used to justify keeping a gumball machine filled with M&Ms in my office for so many years.)

Activities other than exercise and eating chocolate can also increase your body's endorphin levels. Studies show that acupuncture, massage therapy, meditation, and sex can stimulate endorphin secretion.

# "BAD" DISTRESS CHEMICALS

When you work with bullies, you can forget about having a nice flow of eustress chemicals. You also don't get a healthy little shot of adrenaline and a little shot of cortisol. Instead, when you experience chronic or ongoing distress, you get a flood of adrenaline and cortisol rushing throughout your body and brain.

> **That is actually what it is called "flooding," which is the exact opposite of Flow.**

When we see a danger approaching, such as a troll, our brain perceives this person as a threat. Remember: Our brains have not really changed in 5,000 years. Our brains do not recognize the difference between a saber tooth tiger and some idiot on the expressway cutting us off in traffic. All it knows is that you are in danger, so the fight-or-flight response is initiated.

Our bodies need a moderate level of cortisol to function properly. Cortisol also acts like a biological "fuel" for our metabolism and helps us to properly regulate our immune system and to seal in emotional memories. However, having cortisol in your brain is a lot like drinking water. A certain amount of water each day is good for us—but not if you try drinking it from a fire hydrant.

## WHY HUMANS GET ULCERS AND ZEBRAS DON'T

We all have distress in our lives. It is unavoidable, and our bodies were designed to take and even be invigorated by short-term distress. Often, we can actually perform better thanks to short-term distress. Therefore, having moderate stress in our lives can actually be very good for us.

When we experience short-term distress, our sympathetic nervous system kicks in and prepares us for fight-or-flight, just like it did for our cavemen and women ancestors years ago. Our brain then puts our adrenal glands, which are located just above the kidneys, on high alert, thinking that we are under attack. Adrenaline and cortisol will then surge into our system in as little as 17,000ths of a second to get us ready for what it believes is an impending attack. Our fight-or-flight response and our emotional system are at least twice as fast as our logical brain.[26]

Due to the increased flow of these various chemicals, our senses are greatly heightened. We become more focused, sharper. We can become invigorated, which is why we spend so much time and money each year riding roller coasters, bungee jumping off bridges, and even skydiving. When the perceived danger subsides, our parasympathetic nervous system kicks in, which restores our system to a state of rest and relaxation. We typically refer to this restorative state of equilibrium as "homeostasis." (Yes, for all of the purists out there, I will use this more common term of "homeostasis" throughout this book because it is better known to everyone. However, the more all-encompassing term used by many neuroscientists today is "allostasis.")

This is how our nervous system responds to "acute distress," which means the distress is short-lived and we can go back to a "normal" and relaxed state soon after the danger disappears. Acute stress can be life threatening, such as when we are attacked by a lion. In such situations, our entire fight-or-flight system kicks into gear, which means our heart rate soars, the blood is immediately sent to the large skeletal muscles and our lungs, and we either fight or run for our lives. In these situations, our body knows that many of our other long-term bodily functions don't matter, such as our growth, reproductive and digestive systems, which is why our mouth goes dry when we are under stress. If the danger passes, then we can return to a state of homeostasis and these longer-term functions can return. If we are eaten, then they won't matter anymore anyway. From a purely logical standpoint, it is a great system.

In rare cases, when children are exposed to severe ongoing distress, they can develop "stress dwarfism." When children are forced to endure tremendous chronic distress, their pituitary gland will shut down the child's growth hormone for long periods of time. As a result, the child's growth can be stunted. This was the case with *Peter Pan* author J.M. Barry. Barry's homelife as a child was so horrendous that the chronic distress he suffered actually stunted his growth to the point that he never grew past five feet tall. Now you know some of the tragedy behind the real Peter Pan.[27]

Therefore, eustress is like getting on a roller coaster and then getting off again after about a two-minute ride. Distress, or chronic stress, is like getting on a roller coaster ride . . . and not getting off for a week.

However, the greatest threat for most of us in today's world is unique to the human animal: psychological stress. Most animals will go into fight-or-flight mode in response to a short-term physical threat. We see this all the time on National Geographic specials. We see a zebra out walking on the Serengeti when a pride of lions suddenly come out of nowhere and rip the little zebra to shreds. Believe me, this is a case of acute distress for the zebra.

In his book, *Why Don't Zebras Get Ulcers? Why Do We?* Dr. Robert Sapolsky explains that zebras don't get ulcers because like most animals, they live in the moment. They do not sit around and worry about the bullies they see every day that really might kill them. They are cautious because they are not stupid. However, they do not get ulcers because they do not lose sleep worrying if they will survive tomorrow. They don't worry about their retirement, their overall health, what that thing is stuck to their hoof, and so on.

Humans, thanks to our highly developed brains, and in particular our frontal lobes, worry about everything. Most of us do not experience great physical threats like the rest of the animal kingdom. Instead, we humans routinely activate our fight-or-flight system for pure psychological reasons, and that is not what our system was designed to do. Other animals are knocked out of homeostasis because they are physically forced to react. Humans today do it primarily because we **worry** about being attacked.

This is how I learned not to watch National Geographic specials with my sons. As we watched one program, we saw the beautifully photographed gazelles raising their young, eating dinner with them, and playing with their little gazelles. It was amazing and my youngest son, Nicholas, was smiling and laughing . . . right up until the hyenas charged in and ripped one of the baby gazelles in two. Even though we live in Ohio and Tanzania is about 8,000 miles away, Nicholas was afraid of being eaten by hyenas for about a month after that. And no, it did not help to remind him that the mommy gazelle still had two other babies, so losing only one of them wasn't so bad.

Neuroscience can now show us the truth of the adage:
**"Attitude is everything."**

## THE ROSETO EFFECT:
## SOCIAL EPIGENETICS IN ACTION

Perhaps the best example of "social epigenetics" that I have ever seen comes from Malcolm Gladwell's book, *Outliers*. In his book, Gladwell discusses the "Roseto Effect."

In the late 1800s, some Italians from the small town of Roseto immigrated to the United States. They then traveled west and found jobs in a slate quarry near Bangor, Pennsylvania. As more jobs became available, more Italian immigrants came from Roseto to Pennsylvania. Bangor was filled with so many Roseto immigrants that the area was renamed Roseto, Pennsylvania.

In the late 1950s, Stewart Wolf, a physician from the University of Oklahoma who owned a farm near Roseto, spent his summer breaks there. Wolf, who taught his classes about the human digestive system, was invited to give a talk to the local physicians. As he was talking to the local doctors after the meeting, one of them told Wolf, "You know, I've been practicing for seventeen years. I get patients from all over, and I rarely find anyone from Roseto under the age of sixty-five with heart disease."

In the 1950s, heart disease was the leading cause of death for men under the age of sixty-five. This was years before physicians were prescribing any cholesterol lowering drugs and recommending the various healthy heart practices we all know about today. It was simply unbelievable that the people of Roseto had virtually no heart disease under the age of 65.

Wolf wanted to investigate. So, in 1961, he brought in some of his students and colleagues to discover why there was no heart disease in Roseto. Wolf and his team researched the death certificates of the people living in Roseto going back years. They reviewed their physicians' records and they took medical histories on their entire families.

The people of Roseto were so very excited over participating in this study that they fully cooperated with Wolf's team. The town even suspended their council meetings so Wolf and his team would have the space they needed to work. The people set up booths in Roseto's town hall so Wolf's team could draw blood, perform EEGs, and run other medical tests.

The ladies of Roseto even supplied the entire team with lunch. Even the mayor's sisters volunteered to help.

Wolf's time frame for completing these tests and collecting data ran way past his four-week schedule. So, the people of Roseto let Wolf and his team use the local school for the summer to continue their work. When the team invited everyone living in Roseto to come and be tested, everyone flooded to the school.

The town of Roseto could not have been more cooperative and inviting to Wolf and his team. They welcomed Wolf and his team like family.

What Wolf and his team discovered was amazing. Just as Wolf had been told earlier, no one under the age of 65 in Roseto had **ever** died from a heart attack or even showed any signs of heart disease. Even for those men 65 years of age or older, the death rate from heart disease in Roseto was only about half of what the rest of the United States was experiencing.

Even though Wolf had shown there was little heart disease in Roseto, he still had not discovered why. So, Wolf brought in a friend of his to help find the answer: John Bruhn, a sociologist from Oklahoma.

Bruhn and Wolf hired medical students, and some sociology graduate students, to continue the interviews with the people of Roseto. These students went from house to house and talked to every person who was at least 21 years of age. Everyone was interviewed.

What Bruhn and Wolf discovered was even more amazing than their conclusions regarding Roseto's low rate of heart disease:

> **There was literally no suicide,
> no alcoholism, no drug addiction,
> no peptic ulcers, and very little crime
> in Roseto.**

Bruhn and Wolf then hypothesized as to why these amazing phenomena were happening in Roseto.

First, Wolf reasoned that the people of Roseto must have held on to some special dietary practices from Italy that kept them healthier than the rest of the United States. However, this theory quickly fell apart when he saw that the people of Roseto were actually doing everything that modern medicine said would give them heart disease. It was like they were trying to kill themselves. They cooked with lard, instead of using the much healthier olive oil they would have typically used back in the old country. In fact, 41% of these people's calories came from saturated fat.

Also, the pizza they ate back in Italy was much healthier than what they were eating here in America. In Italy, the pizza they ate was made with a thin crust covered with salt, oil, and maybe some tomatoes, anchovies, or onions. The pizza they ate in America was a thick breaded dough loaded with sausage, pepperoni, salami, ham, and sometimes eggs. It was a killer.

Back in Italy, they ate sweets like biscotti and taralli, which is a pretzel-like snack—and only then on special holidays like Christmas and Easter. In America, they ate these sweets, and many others, all year round.

Wolf also discovered these people didn't exercise regularly, they smoked heavily, and many were considerably overweight.

These people seemed to violate all of the rules in trying to prevent heart disease, but still, they were mostly immune to it.

Clearly, the answer to their astonishing health and their longevity did not lie in their diet or exercise.

In the end, Wolf realized that the secret to the health of the people living in Roseto wasn't diet, exercise, their genes, or the region where they lived. Wolf realized that the secret to the health of the people living in Roseto had nothing to do with modern medicine's approach to health.

Instead, the answer to these people's astonishingly good health was more in the world of sociology than in the medical field:

> **The secret to their amazingly good health rested in the attitudes of the people living in Roseto themselves.**

The same cooperation and hospitality Wolf and his team experienced when they first came to town was the same reason the people of Roseto were so healthy and lived so long.

As Bruhn and Wolf walked around the town, they focused on how the people of Roseto visited and interacted with each other. They stopped to chat with one another in their native Italian right there on the street. They cooked for each other in their backyards. They passed on stories about their extended families that formed the foundation of the town's social structure. They noticed that many homes had three generations living under one roof, and how much respect grandparents were given by the younger members of the town. They regularly went to mass at Our Lady of Mt. Carmel Church and saw the unifying and calming effect of the church. Bruhn and Wolf saw there were 22 civic organizations in a town that had less than 2,000 people. They saw a clear "egalitarian ethos" throughout the town that discouraged the wealthy from flaunting their success. Instead, they helped those who had been less successful.

Today, we identify what the people of Roseto experience every day as being eustress, and the world of neuroscience can now show why Wolf and Bruhn were right. The cocktail of chemicals that flow through our bodies when we experience eustress can have a more powerful effect on our health than our bad diets, smoking and lack of exercise.

Remember: Every thought you have is a chemical and electrical reaction in your body. Social epigenetics tells us that our bodies, which includes our brain, will adapt themselves to their surroundings.

So, what kind of surroundings are you creating for yourself?

For me, understanding the power of eustress chemicals only motivated me more to make my work as enjoyable as possible and to help others who need it. And, of course, to . . .

> **Get as many jackasses out of my life as possible.**

# 4

## HOW DISTRESS IS KILLING YOU!

When I first started educating myself in brain health, I had no idea how distress was killing me—and you. Then I understood how destructive the negative "bullies" we all work with can be to our overall health.

I soon learned to think whenever I got that tight feeling in my gut, like whenever I had to deal with the bullies in my life:

> **I am smoking a cigarette.**

With all the research conducted on the disastrous effects chronic distress has on our health, it is clear that the distress we experience due to our contact with trolls is killing us—literally. Several studies show this chronic ongoing distress is worse for our health than smoking. In one study, researchers found that cigarette smoking increases your mortality rate by a factor of 1.6, which means cigarette smoking will increase your chance of premature death by 60%. (Everyone has a mortality factor of 1.0, which we really don't like to think about too much.) However, in this study, the distress experienced by the subjects increased their mortality rate by a factor of 2.0.[28]

> **Chronic distress can *double* your chance of dying prematurely, which is 40% worse for your health than smoking.**

According to Dr. Ronald Siegel, Psy.D. of Harvard Medical School, 80% of all doctor's visits are distress related. Distress is the primary cause of such conditions as chronic neck and back pain, gastrointestinal disorders, headaches, insomnia, and sexual disfunction, to mention a few.[29]

Quite frankly, it is better to sit with the smokers than the bullies.

Still, we continue to treat smokers like social lepers, but then welcome these lethal bullies into our lives. Many of us will not let anyone smoke in our homes. Employers almost universally ban smoking in the workplace, and some even refuse to hire smokers. However, we not only welcome bullies into our lives, we actually protect them and refuse to address their mortal attacks.

I have encountered many bullies as part of my practice. When I confront them with their unacceptable behavior, 90% of the time they go on the offensive. They attack back. The most common type of attack is to "Kill the Messenger." They will say things like, "He yelled at me!" or "He was mean to me!"

Of course, they do this because they cannot refute the message, so they attack and lie about the messenger. Unfortunately, in most instances, poor leaders fall for this smoke screen because, well, no one should ever be upset. In the end, the bullies win. That is a critical lack of leadership, and it is deadly for the good employees who have to work with these trolls.

If you find yourself in a workplace where you are being bullied by trolls, and the leadership will not address the issue, give them copies of my first two books, *Solve Employee Problems*

*Before They Start* and *Living The Five Skills of Tolerance,* as well as a copy of this book. Then watch what happens. If the leadership is not going to address these issues, then find another job.

Yes, as you will see, your number-one health risk actually comes from the chronic distress in your life, which largely comes from the bullies. Your life really does depend on surrounding yourself with supportive and tolerant people.

It amazes me how we all respond immediately whenever someone is physically punched by a bully, whether it is at school, at work, or in our private lives. We all recognize that as being a terrible act of violence. However, if I had the choice, it is better to be physically punched by a bully than to be punched in the self-esteem. The chronic distress from having your dignity violated is much worse for your overall health because the humiliation will more than likely haunt your thoughts for a long, long time.

Remember Rule #1: Get as many jackasses out of my life as possible.

## INTERPERSONAL VS. IMPERSONAL DISTRESS

When placed under chronic distress, our brain puts us in a state of "high alert." Our brain automatically orders our bodies (specifically, our endocrine system) to release a flood of hormones, such as adrenaline and cortisol, that prepare us to respond to the perceived emergency or threat. This process is a very effective way to prepare our bodies for fight-or-flight. Our body simply does not recognize the difference between an attack from a saber tooth tiger or from a bully. It only differentiates between the various degrees of a threat. Unfortunately, when our body concentrates so many of its resources on preparing us for fight-or-flight, it "borrows" resources from other bodily systems, such as our immune system. The systems primarily responsible for maintaining our health are greatly weakened, either for just a few minutes or for years at a time. The reason our body does this is because our brain thinks we are about to get eaten. So, all of our resources are sent to our lungs and large skeletal muscles, because if you get eaten, your immune system becomes irrelevant.

Whenever a study is conducted measuring the stress people experience in different situations, what the researchers are really measuring is how high the subject's levels of adrenaline and cortisol will rise. Over the last several years, numerous studies have been conducted to better understand what levels of stress people typically experience in different situations. We now know that "**inter**personal" distress, or distress that comes from other people, causes our cortisol levels to spike the highest, as opposed to the distress we suffer from "**im**personal" situations, such as when we become frustrated with our work.[30]

In one study when an interviewer treated his interviewees in a disrespectful and hostile manner, the interviewees reacted with some of the highest levels of cortisol of any laboratory stress simulation ever tested. The distress we suffer from other people raises our cortisol levels much higher than the distress we suffer from impersonal conflicts.[31]

In another study, when the researcher criticized the subjects' performance, the subjects' cortisol levels jumped **three times** higher than when their distress was derived exclusively from simply trying to solve an impersonal problem.[32]

So, why is that? Why does our fight-or-flight system react so much more severely when people are involved? Because our brain knows that other people might kill you. Your computer won't.

The "impersonal" conflicts we have with inanimate objects are soon forgotten.

> **However, the shame and offenses suffered from other people, or interpersonal conflicts, will increase our stress levels by as much as three times higher than those we suffer from inanimate objects.**

Therefore, when we experience impersonal stress, such as when our car will not start, or when we have a heavy workload, our most basic need for acceptance and safety is not being threatened, so the level of distress we experience is not as great. The distress we suffer from mere objects is only about 30% as harmful to us as when the distress comes from another person.

Additionally, studies have shown that once our body goes into a state of fight-or-flight, which happens to most people when our heart rate hits about 145 beats per minute, it takes about 40 minutes for our brain to recover from the massive amounts of cortisol we produce from impersonal stress. However, when the source of the distress is from another human, the cortisol level stayed elevated in the subjects' bodies **50% longer, taking up to an hour or more to return to normal.**[33]

> **This means that once you have gone into fight-or-flight, you really should not have any interactions with anyone else for at least an hour.**[34]

If this distress continues and our heart rate hits about 175 beats per minute, we become what is called "temporarily autistic," according to Dr. Keith Payne, Professor of Psychology and Neuroscience at the University of North Carolina. When this happens to us, we start to experience an absolute break-down of our cognitive processing. We have what feels like an out-of-body experience. Everything slows down so we can give our undivided attention to whatever is threatening us. Time seems to stand still. Everything becomes surreal. In this case, you should probably not have any serious interactions with anyone else for the rest of the day.[35]

Clearly, not all distress is the same. The most harmful distress we experience is the stress we get from trolls, or bullies. *THAT* is the stress that kills us—and we do it to ourselves.

# FIVE HEALTH RISKS FROM TROLLS

## HEALTH RISK #1: HEART DISEASE AND STROKE

Do trolls actually give us heart disease and strokes? YES!

In recent years, researchers have been able to identify why the distress we suffer gives us heart disease and a height-ened susceptibility to strokes. In both Sweden and the United Kingdom, civil service workers at different levels in their orga-nizations were studied to determine their levels of job distress in what is now called the "Whitehall Study." The first Whitehall Study, which is referred to as Whitehall I, was originally con-ducted by Professor Sir Michael Marmot over a ten-year period starting in 1967. This study examined over 17,500 male civil servants between the ages of 20 and 64. A second study, the Whitehall II Study, was conducted from 1985 to 1988 and exam-ined the health of 10,308 civil servants aged 35 to 55, of whom two-thirds were men and one-third women.[36]

The study was a perfect comparison of how various levels of a social hierarchy correspond directly with different levels of distress. Everyone employed in these civil service systems had identical health care coverage. They all lived in the same general geographic area. Gender differences were evenly distributed throughout the organization. Younger people were employed at the lower levels of these organizations, so you would naturally expect their health to be better than their older superiors.

However, the study discovered that those workers in the lower-level positions were **four times** more likely to develop cardiovascular disease than those who were in the top rungs of the organization. What accounted for the difference? Those people positioned in the upper tiers of the organization didn't have to put up with the whims of their superiors as much as those in the lower ranks. Those in the higher ranks had more control over their work and how they were treated.

The study discovered that those workers in the lower levels of the system could be told to do things just because someone in a higher-ranking position "felt like it," which meant the level of supervisory skill that the supervisors at the lower levels possessed was not as great as those at the higher levels. Therefore, the people in the lower levels of these organizations were more susceptible to being "bullied" on a frequent basis, which subjected them to chronic distress.

The study concluded that workers who felt they were being treated unfairly, or were wrongly criticized, or whose boss would not listen to their problems, had a **30%** higher rate of coronary heart disease than those who felt they had been treated fairly and were not being "bullied" as much.

Research since then has supported the Whitehall Study findings. Actually, studies show that the people with some of the highest levels of distress are working in highly demanding positions where they have little control over their work. This is typical of middle managers. However, those who have highly demanding jobs but also have a high level of control over their work have much lower levels of distress.

> **Therefore, the more control one has over their own work, the more that person's distress levels drop.**

Interestingly, studies also show that whenever someone is bullied, it is actually a very good outlet for them to **bully someone else**. Yes, once you have been bullied by someone, it will help your own system if you then beat on one of your co-workers or subordinates. Why is this so? Because thousands of years ago, if Barney Rubble ever bullied Fred Flintstone, Fred would simply kill him. That would actually make the world safe again for Fred: The threat was dead.[37]

This is one reason why bullying can spread through a society or workplace like wildfire. As a result . . .

> **We turn on each other like a pack of wild JACKALS!**

This is why it is so important for organizations to deal with their bullies, which include the Attackers and Retreaters, and build a SAFE environment as soon as possible. Otherwise, as people seek retribution and stress relief, they will start bullying each other more and more, either by openly attacking each other or by gossiping with each other like Aunt Bee and all her treacherous friends. The organization will become a death trap.

Recent studies also show that people who are continuously bullied experience a significant rise in their blood pressure, so their blood surges throughout their system at a much faster rate. Throughout our circulatory system, our blood vessels branch out from the "parent" vessels into the smaller "daughter" branches. These are called "bifurcations." When we go into fight-or-flight, our platelets crash into these bifurcations, which look like a "V" in the road, at an accelerated rate. So, our platelets, which are now sticky from the extra adrenaline being pumped into our system, collide into the "V" section of this branch. As these platelets continue to smash into the point of this "V" intersection, the bifurcation becomes damaged and the sticky platelets adhere to the damaged areas. Later, plaque forms around the damaged area, which will start to narrow the blood vessel. Eventually, the narrowing of this area can cut off the blood flow. But that is only one problem that can occur. Another mortal result could be if these platelets and/or plaque break loose and travel to the heart or the brain.[38]

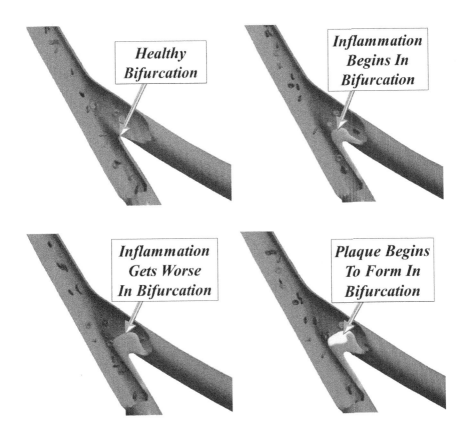

115

As the bullying continues over time, the person being bullied who fails to respond feels less and less able to control the situation. Symptoms of anxiety and depression set in, which will increase their likelihood of cardiovascular disease.

Dr. Carol Shively, professor pathology and psychology at Wake Forest University College of Medicine, has studied the physical effects distress has on the body. In performing her research, she studied the social habits of macaque monkeys and the biological effects chronic distress had on them. She studied macaque monkeys because they live in a social hierarchy and are very social animals, just like humans. What she discovered was amazing.[39]

Shively first discovered that the dominant monkeys were much more social and alert. They were more upbeat and active. However, just as in the Whitehall Study, those monkeys who found themselves at the bottom of the pecking order grew depressed due to the constant bullying they received. This chronic distress inflicted upon them by the more dominant monkeys not only put them into a state of symptomatic depression, but it also destroyed their overall health.

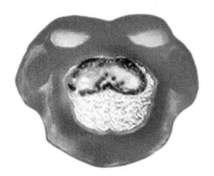 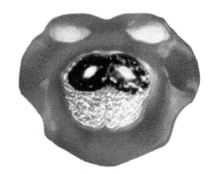

DOMINANT                SUBORDINATE

Dr. Shively then scanned the brains of the dominant and subordinate monkeys. As shown in the graphic on the left, the dominant monkey's brain was well lit and was very active in the frontal lobe portion of the brain, which is the portion our brain uses for reasoning and logic. However, the subordinate monkey on the right is not generating nearly as much activity as the dominant monkey's frontal lobes. So, what accounts for this difference?

According to Dr. Shively, the dominant monkeys were not being bullied or belittled, so their brains were generating a healthy amount of dopamine, the "reward" chemical that motivates us to excel. The subordinate monkey's brain, on the other hand, simply was not generating nearly as much dopamine as the dominant monkeys, so the subordinate monkeys were experiencing severe symptoms of depression.

The strain of being belittled, being forced to serve in a subordinate role and being subjected to the whims of the dominant monkeys was creating a dangerous shortage of such eustress chemicals as dopamine. This caused depression to set in for the subordinate monkeys, just as it did for the civil service workers who were subjected to the whims and unfair criticisms of their superiors.

**Subordinate Distressed Macaque Artery**     **Dominant Healthy Macaque Artery**

Dr. Shively also discovered that the subordinate monkeys developed heart disease at least **twice** as fast as the dominant monkeys. The distress of being bullied and abused by the dominant monkeys was flooding their systems with adrenaline and cortisol to where they were at much greater risk of heart attack and stroke—just like humans.[40]

High levels of chronic distress can also destroy heart muscle. After each launch at NASA, it was common that about 15% of employees would lose their jobs. This added stress caused many health problems among the NASA employees. Actually, the health of the NASA employees got so bad that the leadership thought the Russians were poisoning their water. However, the autopsies conducted on the NASA employees who passed away revealed these chronically high levels of distress destroyed their heart muscle. Such high levels of distress, which resulted in massive amounts of adrenaline and cortisol rushing through their systems, scarred the inside of the heart muscle wall.[41]

At the same time we experience these constant and heightened levels of distress, the walls of our blood vessels secrete substances that bind themselves to our T-cells, which play a critical role in our immune system and we will discuss in more detail later. Because of this increased number of T-cells and the substances secreted by our blood vessels, we form artery-clogging plaque on our endothelium, which is the thin layer of cells that line the interior of our blood vessels. This damaging physiological process created by distress lays the foundation for arteriosclerosis.[42]

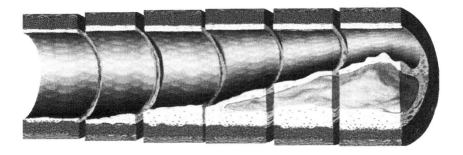

**ARTERIOSCLEROSIS: Progression Of Build Up On The Endothelium**

Further, our body begins flooding our system with adrenaline and cortisol when our heart rate rises at about ten beats per minute above what it would normally be when we are calm and at rest.[43]

On average, a woman's heart rate at rest is about 82 beats per minute, while a man's average heart rate at rest is about 72 beats per minute. However, as we are placed under distress, our adrenal glands begin to secrete adrenaline, or pure energy. This speeds up our heart rate.

Again, our bodies respond this way to protect us. They are trying to save us from a suspected danger. If this was 5,000 years ago, we would go into fight-or-flight and burn most of this adrenaline and cortisol off. Today, we typically go back to our work areas and let this adrenaline and cortisol fester, which causes us many problems.

When we go into fight-or-flight, our heart rate can jump from 10 to 30 beats in one heartbeat. When our blood vessels expand so quickly, what do you think this rapid expansion does to them?[44]

Think of it this way: What would happen to a garden hose if you threw it out into the snow, let it freeze, and then brought it back into the house and let it thaw? After it thaws out, you then throw the hose back out into the snow, let it freeze, then drag it back in again and let it thaw again. What would happen if you did this two or three times?

Clearly, the garden hose would crack and break. That is also what happens throughout your circulatory system, especially around your heart. You get little "micro tears" in your blood vessels.

Unfortunately, these little micro tears present many problems for us.

First, these micro tears cause little barbs to protrude out from the inside walls of our blood vessels. Over the years, the plaque that flows through our blood stream will get caught on these little barbs and build up. This is also the beginning of arteriolosclerosis.

Then, on Sunday evening, we get that tight feeling in our gut just over the thought of going back into that "hell hole" tomorrow, so the adrenaline and cortisol build up in our blood stream. Due to the increased T-cells and cortisol being released, our blood will then thicken throughout the night. Since we are going into fight-or-flight, our body thinks we might get bit in an impending attack. Our body actually does this to protect us so our blood will clot more easily if we are wounded. However, we do not burn off this cortisol by running away or fighting. Instead, we go to bed.

Then, about 3:00, 4:00, or 5:00 in the morning, "Bang!" There's your Monday morning heart attack or stroke. (Now you know why we have so many heart attacks on Monday morning.)

But then, this shouldn't be that much of a problem, right? I mean, today we have "Plavix." That should keep our blood nice and slippery, right?

Well, actually such drugs as Plavix do a great job in preventing heart attacks and strokes. However, the problem is that we still have these weakened walls in our blood vessels since they have been drastically expanding and contracting over the years. As a result, you might not have a heart attack on Monday morning. Instead, one of these weakened blood vessels can simply "pop," which we call an "aneurism."

So, which is worse, having a heart attack or just having a blood vessel pop?

Either way . . . Congratulations! You don't have to go to work!

Clearly, this chronic distress we experience today is literally destroying our cardiovascular health.

## HEALTH RISK #2: GETTING SICK!

Chronic distress can also make us sick, exacerbate our autoimmune diseases, and, according to some of the latest research, actually cause us to contract an autoimmune disease.[45]

How the immune system works is a tremendously complicated topic, so I will speak in more general terms in order to simplify how chronic distress is harming our immune system.

Today, we understand that our immune system is controlled by our central nervous system. Our central nervous system talks to our immune system and tells it what to do.

Whenever our central nervous system senses that our body has been "invaded" by some foreign entity, or pathogen, it dispatches our immune system to combat the evil invaders, which are usually viruses and bacteria. The first to arrive on the scene, or our body's emergency responder, is called our "adaptive immune system." There are two broad types of adaptive immune cells we will look at here:

- Our "B lymphocytes," or "B-cells," which mature in our bone marrow, and
- Our "T lymphocytes," or our "T-cells," which come from our thymus, which explains why they are called B-cells and T-cells.

Easy, right?

Together, they make up about 20% to 40% of our white blood cells. About 80% of our adaptive immune system's cells are T-cells and about 20% are B-cells.[46]

Our B-cells are our body's sentinels. They travel throughout our body on patrol looking for intruders. When they spot an intruder, they make antibodies designed to kill that specific foreign invader. These antibodies will then call for help from the more lethal T-cells, which will rush to the area and blow the trespassers to bits. Yes, our T-cells are the Abram tanks of our immune system.

Since these pathogens are about to get blown to smithereens by our T-cells, some of them are not going to just sit there and wait for this to happen. Instead, they will sometimes try to disguise themselves and hide. One type of bacteria will actually change the types of proteins living on its surface to keep the T-cells from recognizing them. So, when the B-cells identify the proteins on the bacteria and call in the T-cells to fight, by the time the T-cells arrive, the bacteria will have changed the protein living on their surface so the T-cells won't recognize them. That is basically the equivalent of a B-cell recognizing a criminal on the street, the B-cell calls the police, or the T-cell, but by the time the police get there, the bacteria has put on Groucho Marx glasses in hopes of not being recognized.

This is called the "coevolution of pathogens."[47]

The other and older part of our immune system is our "innate immune system." Our innate immune system kicks into gear and works to inflame the entire area that has been damaged. This inflammation acts as a physical barrier to protect us and keep other pathogens from entering through the wounded area. An example of this is when you sprain an ankle. Because of the sprain, the ankle will swell up in an effort to protect itself so you don't keep making the sprain worse.[48]

So, what happens when you get an invader, like a bully at work yelling at you, and you go into fight-or-flight? You feel your gut tense up, so your body floods with adrenaline and cortisol. This surge of cortisol kills off your old immune cells, which activates your B-cells, who then call up the Abram tank T-cells to protect you. When this chronic distress continues, we use up too many of the T-cells, so they are not available to fight off other germs and viruses. That is when we get "run down," get sick and inflammation can begin.

Therefore, having too much cortisol in our body is clearly a problem. That is why chronic distress can throw our immune systems into overdrive and use up our valuable resources, like our T-cells, so there is very little left to fight real disease.

In one study, volunteers for an experiment involving distress were falsely accused of shoplifting. As the volunteers tried to defend themselves against the false charges, their immune and cardiovascular systems mobilized in a potentially deadly combination. Their immune systems secreted a heightened number of T-cells in response to this short-term state of distress.[49]

In a study conducted at The Ohio State University, researchers discovered that roommates who disliked each other became ill much more frequently than those students who lived with roommates they liked. Of course, this meant the sick roommates probably had to spend even more time together![50]

Studies also reveal that if you have an ongoing personal conflict with another person that lasts for one month or longer, you have just increased your chance of becoming ill, such as catching a cold, by as much as **2.5 times**.[51]

However, while ongoing arguments and feuds are bad for our health, **isolating** ourselves from human contact is actually worse. Studies show those people with the fewest close relationships were **4.2 times** more likely to come down with a cold, making loneliness riskier than smoking. Therefore, even if you avoid the trolls at work and isolate yourself, that will only make things worse for you if you deprive yourself of a positive support system. A lack of positive human contact is just as damaging as the distress we experience from working with trolls because it deprives us of the eustress chemicals we humans desperately need to remain healthy.[52]

We all need to think about that as many of us tend to telecommute more and more due to our COVID isolation.

The more we socialize with positive and supportive people, the less susceptible to colds and illnesses we become. Why? Because vibrant social relationships boost our good moods by emitting positive eustress chemicals throughout our bodies. This enhances our immune functions, largely because our T-cells can now focus on fighting real disease rather than wasting their resources on fighting the excess cortisol in our bodies.

At The Ohio State University, psychologist Janice Kiecolt-Glaser and her husband, immunologist Ronald Glaser, conducted one of the most important studies ever done on distress and our immune systems. The OSU team studied one group of women in their sixties who were caring for their husbands with Alzheimer's disease. The caregivers were under tremendous stress from their 24-hour-a-day duties. More importantly, they were all feeling isolated and uncared for themselves.[53]

The OSU researchers discovered that the women who were caretakers had 50% less of what I will refer to as the "G-gene" in their systems than other women their age. The G-gene regulates many of our immune functions by producing lymphocytes and boosting our body's T-cells, which destroy invading bacteria and viruses. The Ohio State researchers found that the G-genes of these caregivers were greatly reduced due to the chronic distress they were under, which is why it took these caregivers **nine days** longer to heal from a small puncture wound than the women in the non-distressed comparison group.

The researchers found that the constant distress suffered by these caregivers in social isolation impaired their brain's ability to regulate the production of cortisol, which resulted in more flooding for these women. Their immune system genes, such as the G-gene, could not effectively fight off real diseases.

Likewise, in an earlier study of women under similar distressful conditions, researchers discovered that they did not even benefit from getting flu shots. Their immune system had deteriorated so much that they could not manufacture the antibodies the vaccination ordinarily stimulates.[54]

As the bully continues to abuse you, your other and older immune system, the "innate immune" system, which I will call your "inflammation system," also identifies what it finds in your body as being either a friend or a foe. This immune system causes parts of your body to become inflamed to block out other invaders. As this chronic distress keeps making more cortisol, your immune system keeps trying to get rid of it, and your inflammation system can become confused. As a result, your inflammation system can start identifying parts of your body that are supposed to be there, or "friends," as being "foes." So, your inflammation system will then start attacking those areas as if they were invaders, or pathogens. Yes, our inflammation system attacks our own body because it is overworked and becomes disoriented.[55]

If someone already has an autoimmune disease, which is a condition where the body is basically attacking itself, such as with multiple sclerosis or rheumatoid arthritis, this added distress can cause these conditions to flare up. Therefore, even though our inflammation system is all about inflaming our injured areas to protect them, chronic distress can confuse this system and turn it against us. Our body will inflame healthy areas that you really do not want to become inflamed. So, any areas that already have an autoimmune issue become even more inflamed.

At the other end of the spectrum, not having enough cortisol in our system can be just as bad as having too much. We need a certain level of cortisol to return our immune system back to its normal baseline after we have gone into fight-or-flight. If our system continues to work in overdrive and we have used up too much of the cortisol, our immune system cannot adequately return to normal. When this happens, if you are already prone towards having some kind of autoimmune disorder, or if you already have too much inflammation in your body, your immune system can continue to attack you and maybe cause you to contract an autoimmune disease.

Chronic psychological distress has long been suspected of being a cause of autoimmune disease. Many retrospective studies have found up to an 80% correlation to exist between patients reporting high degrees of emotional distress occurring just before the onset of the autoimmune disease.[56]

On June 19, 2018, the *Journal of the American Medical Association Network* published a study entitled, "Association of Stress-Related Disorders With Subsequent Autoimmune Disease." In this study, the researchers posed the following question: Are psychiatric reactions induced by trauma or other life stressors associated with subsequent risk of autoimmune disease?

In this Swedish study, researchers studied 106,464 patients with stress-related disorders, and matched these subjects with 1,064,640 individuals who did not have stress-related disorders. These 106,464 patients with stress-related disorders were also compared to 126,652 of their full siblings. The researchers then compared these patients' tendency to develop autoimmune diseases at least one year later when compared to these other groups. The researchers concluded that having chronically high levels of distress gave these patients a significantly higher risk of acquiring an autoimmune disease. Therefore, the study concluded that stress-related disorders were significantly associated with the risk of acquiring a subsequent autoimmune disease.

Interestingly, this belief that the immune system can be fooled is not a new concept. In the "rose" study conducted back in the 1800s, people who were allergic to roses had artificial roses waved in front of their noses. Even though these people did not know these roses were fake, they suddenly had allergic reactions to the "rose," which included sneezing. Yes, our immune system can be fooled into attacking something that is not real.

Therefore, it is clear:

> **Distress from trolls makes you sick!**
> **The lack of eustress, which includes the lack of positive human interaction, also makes you sick!**

## HEALTH RISK #3: AGING BEYOND YOUR YEARS

Have you ever noticed how much the President of the United States has aged after only four years in office? Doesn't it look as if he has aged at least eight years? In reality, he has.

**1860**          **1864**          **1865**

When humans find themselves subjected to ongoing and endless distress, the excess cortisol produced by our bodies strikes at the very core of our DNA. When our bodies continue to flood with adrenaline and cortisol, our cells have to fight to neutralize and eject these excess chemicals from our systems. The rate at which our cells age is accelerated, which adds years to our biological age. Researchers studying the DNA of mothers caring for chronically ill children found that the longer they had been caring for these children, the more the cells in these women had aged way beyond their actual chronological years.[57]

In determining our biological age, scientists measure the length of the telomeres on our white blood cells. A telomere is the protective end of a chromosome. Telomeres act as protective caps on our chromosomes, keeping our DNA from unraveling, much like the plastic protective ends of our shoestrings, or aglets, which keep the laces themselves from fraying.[58]

However, whenever a cell divides to duplicate itself, a little bit of the telomere is worn away. Without these telomeres, cells can't continue their duplication process because there is nothing to hold the chromosomes together. In other words, our telomeres act like the caps on the ends of our chromosomes keeping all of our DNA contained safely inside.

Our cells continue to reproduce again and again throughout their life spans to heal wounds and fight disease along with our white blood cells. The cells in our bodies can reproduce anywhere between 10 to 50 times each, depending on the cell involved. However, after the cell has reproduced the maximum number of times, that is it. It can never replicate itself again because the cell's telomeres have become too short to protect the ends of the chromosomes. The cell simply unravels, or "retires," which means the cell has lost its ability to reproduce.

**TELOMERES "SHRINKING AWAY" FROM CHROMOSOMES**

In determining the biological age of mothers caring for their chronically ill children, researchers examined the telomeres on the mothers' white blood cells. The researchers discovered that the mothers acting as caregivers had actually aged an average of **ten full years** more than women who were their same chronological age but were not placed under such high levels of interpersonal distress.[59]

Based upon research conducted by Dr. Robert Sapolsky at Stanford University, it is estimated that for every year you spend in high-distress environments, your body can age up to **six years** biologically.[60]

Think about that:

> **For every year you age chronologically in high distress environments, you can actually cut six years off your life.**

Why did these caregivers age so rapidly? Their cells were duplicating themselves at such a heightened rate in order to combat the excess adrenaline and cortisol that their cells were also using up all of their telomeres and thus their reproductive lives. This also explains why we look at the President of the United States after four years in office and say, "Wow, look how much he has aged." The President has most likely aged at least eight years across the last four due to the chronic distress he has had to endure.

Therefore, you really can "age beyond your years"—and for most of us, trolls play a big part in doing that to us.

However, the researchers also found a critical exception to their findings:

> **The mothers caring for their chronically ill children who also had the moral support of others aged no faster than anyone else their age.**

What made this difference? Eustress.

First, the moral support of other humans releases tremendously positive eustress chemicals in our bodies, which include oxytocin, dopamine, and others. These eustress chemicals make us better able to battle the excess distress chemicals of adrenaline and cortisol. That is why we feel refreshed when we get the support and encouragement from the positive people in our lives. Eustress chemicals make all the difference.

Additionally, in 1985, two researchers, Carol W. Greider and Elizabeth Blackburn, discovered a chemical released into our bodies when we feel the moral support of others. This chemical actually bonds to and protects the telomeres in humans as their cells reproduce. When we humans feel great distress, and we also have the positive support of others, our bodies naturally release a chemical to protect our telomeres from harm. Greider and Blackburn aptly named this enzyme "telomerase."[61]

## TELOMERASE BONDS TO AND PROTECTS OUR TELOMERES

Researchers have discovered that if we have positive ongoing support from others when we are under great distress, not only will telomerase protect our telomeres from unraveling too quickly, but it will also help **rebuild** that part of our telomeres we have lost.

In other words, telomerase can act to rebuild our telomeres. This means . . .

> *The Moral Support of Others Makes*
> *You Younger!*

**TELOMERES BEING PROTECTED AND REBUILT**
**BY TELOMERASE**

Supportive people actually help keep us from growing "old" before our time, and they could even help us to become "younger."

These studies show us the power of having a nice flow of eustress chemicals running throughout our bodies. This positive balance of chemicals we maintain in our bodies is directly related to the attitudes of the people we allow into our lives.

## HEALTH RISK #4: MEMORY LOSS

I forgot what I was going to write here…Oh, yes! Now I remember. (Yeah, bad joke. I know.)

When you get frustrated or flustered, do you forget things? Have you ever wondered why that is—why you can't remember even the simplest of things?

Well, when we have pleasant thoughts and experiences, such as when we work with positive and supportive people, we get a nice flow of adrenaline and cortisol throughout our brain, as well as a nice balance of other eustress chemicals.

However, when we go into distress, or full fight-or-flight, we don't get a nice even flow of adrenaline and cortisol, but instead, our brain floods with these chemicals. Remember: Adrenaline and cortisol are not bad for us. Flooding our bodies and brains with excess adrenaline and cortisol for ongoing periods of time is what harms us. Moderation, moderation, moderation is the key to staying healthy. This raging flood of adrenaline and cortisol energizes your emotions while stifling your short-term working memory transmitter—or your hippocampus.[62]

## THE HIPPOCAMPUS

The hippocampus is located on either side of the thalamus, which is also your limbic or emotional system, right behind the amygdalae, which governs our fight-or-flight response. The hippocampus is primarily involved in storing factual-based memories, which is our short-term working memory, and for transferring new information into our long-term memory system. At best, the hippocampus can typically retain up to seven new pieces of information at a time, which is why telephone numbers for years contained seven digits. This is also why "spaced-time learning" works well whenever someone is being taught many pieces of information.[63]

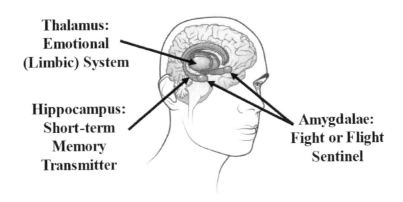

**Thalamus: Emotional (Limbic) System**

**Hippocampus: Short-term Memory Transmitter**

**Amygdalae: Fight or Flight Sentinel**

As most everyone knows, emotions and memory are closely related. This is because our emotional system and our fight-or-flight systems are in close proximity to the hippocampus.

As Joseph Ledoux, a professor and neuroscientist with the Center for Neural Science at New York University, and the researcher who discovered the amygdalae in the 1990s, says, if you see someone you know, the hippocampus recognizes the person, but your emotional system reminds you that you do not like them.

For example, if you go to a party and meet several new people, whose face will you remember? Most likely, you will remember the person who made you laugh, the person who embarrassed you, and the person you were attracted to—all of whom had an emotional impact on you. The emotional impact of events strengthens memory.

The way we humans form memories is pretty straightforward. You sense something that stirs an emotion, which means you have just stimulated your amygdalae and emotional center. This stimulation of the amygdalae results in a little shot of adrenaline and cortisol being secreted across the hippocampus, which literally burns the event into our brain as a memory. The more pronounced the emotion, the more adrenaline and cortisol the body will produce, which will cause the memory to become much more vivid. This is why most people will always remember where they were when they heard about the attack on 9/11, when JFK was assassinated, and so on. We call this a "flashbulb" memory.[64]

Still, even though they work in tandem with one another, our short-term memory and our emotions are two different functions. For instance, if you remember a car crash, the hippocampus allows you to recall the factual events of the accident, such as where it happened, who was involved, etc. However, the amygdalae and the thalamus recall the **fear** associated with the event, thus making it a much stronger memory.

**Dendrites**                              **Axons**

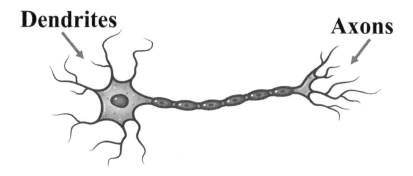

In the graphic above, you will see a single neuron. The way neurons communicate with one another is pretty straightforward. A neuron sends a message out through its axon terminal, or transmitter, which travels into another neuron and enters through its dendrites, or receivers. These axons and dendrites look like several little fingers that stick out from the ends of the neuron. These dendrites fire electronically and "catch" the different signals sent from other neurons. This process is then repeated as this neuron then sends the same signal out through its other end, or axon, which will again be picked up by the dendrites of other neurons. This is not only how our memory system works, but also our entire brain.

Actually, the cells in your central nervous system are the only cells in your body that really do "talk" to each other.

So, what effect do bullies have on this process? First, it is important to understand that your brain is the most fragile organ in your body. It actually has the consistency of soft room-temperature butter. As a result, your brain can easily be damaged by the flooding of chemicals you run through it or by any impacts it suffers. Actually, you have a better chance of damaging your brain than most any other part of your body.

If you want to see how susceptible your brain is to injury, take a little tub of butter out of your refrigerator and set it on your kitchen countertop. Let it sit out overnight. In the morning, drop it onto the floor. Open it up and look inside. That is what we call a "concussion."

As far as the flooding of your brain is concerned, what would happen if you took a cup of gasoline and poured it onto a stick of room temperature butter? It would destroy the butter, wouldn't it? That is basically what this flooding of adrenaline and cortisol does to our brains every day. So, depending on what part of our brain gets damaged, will determine the mental disorder we tend to exhibit.

When bullies increase interpersonal distress in the workplace, this massive flooding of adrenaline and cortisol will overwhelm the neurons of our hippocampus and amygdalae. Since the hippocampus is particularly dense with cortisol receptors, and since it sits right behind the amygdalae, it is easily overwhelmed and flooded with massive amounts of cortisol. When these receptors become overloaded with cortisol, the dendrites in our hippocampus cannot fire properly, so our brain becomes unable to retrieve even the simplest pieces of information while our amygdalae take over and we go on high alert. This can kill the neurons in our hippocampus.

In the end... **VOILA!** Our memory goes to pot and hyper-sensitivity and hyper-vigilance take over. We can actually feel it happening to us, which is why we cannot think straight and we forget things when we get frazzled. We are burning out our short-term memory.[65]

How critical is it to avoid bullies to protect our memory system? In one study conducted by St. Paul's Fire and Marine Insurance Company, when one 700-bed hospital implemented stress reduction and emotional intelligence skills—which means the medical personnel actually had to create a SAFE environment where they started treating each other in a decent manner—**the hospital's medication errors were cut in half.**[66]

In a second study, there was a **70% reduction in malpractice** claims in 22 hospitals that implemented distress prevention activities. In contrast, there was no reduction in claims in a matched group of 22 hospitals that did not implement distress prevention activities.[67]

Why? Because when the doctors, nurses and so on stopped attacking and sniping at one another, their memory systems functioned much better. You simply cannot think clearly and remember even the simplest things if your brain is flooding itself with adrenaline and cortisol.

In 1998, the academic journal *Science* published an article called, "The Biology of Being Frazzled." The article summarized the neurological effects humans experience regarding their thinking and performance whenever they become "frazzled" as opposed to whenever they simply experience the ordinary hassles of daily life. The article concluded that when we humans become "frazzled" we cannot think clearly because we flood our brain. We cannot concentrate and we make many mistakes in the classroom, at the office, in surgery, and so on.

Have you ever wondered why highly competent surgeons will leave "foreign items" in over 1,500 of their patients each year? Before any surgery begins, the surgical team knows exactly how many surgical instruments and sponges they have ready to go. Now, these are highly intelligent surgical teams who have successfully completed years of training. So, why can't such highly intelligent people, people who can transplant organs and repair damaged hearts, count to 25 sponges?[68]

These mistakes create a huge financial liability. On average, leaving objects inside patients can cost as much as $200,000 in medical liability payments for each case.[69]

It is hard to think, or count very well, when you are being bullied and you get frazzled.

To illustrate this point, I will often ask the people attending one of my seminars: "You probably all know what you are supposed to do at stop signs . . . right? You probably also know what you are supposed to do at red lights. So, you could most likely drive me downtown without getting into an accident, getting a ticket, running a red light or getting us killed . . . right?"

The audience will inevitably agree.

I will then ask them, "But what if I verbally abused you the whole way? What if I condescended to you and told you how stupid you were and criticized everything you did? What are the chances we would be in an accident or get a ticket of some kind?"

At this point, someone from the audience inevitably says, "I would throw you out of the car."

My response to that comment is always the same:

**"ABSOLUTELY**! Why we put up with these trolls I will never know. If the bullies, or trolls, in our lives do not change their ways . . . **THROW THEM OUT OF THE CAR!"** (Figuratively, of course.)

In the vast majority of our daily situations, the difference between our success and failure depends on whether we flood from distress or get into the Flow with eustress.

This is why the late quality-control guru W. Edwards Deming adopted the slogan:

> **"Banish fear."**

Deming believed that fear could "freeze" an entire workplace. How does this "freeze effect" present itself? When fear dominates the workplace, when it is not SAFE, workers are reluctant to speak up, to share new ideas, or to coordinate their efforts with others. Improving quality becomes impossible. This same logic applies to every aspect of our lives:

> **Fear frazzles the mind and destroys learning.**

Deming was right. However, today, we have neuroscience to show why.

Our brain doesn't flood and thus frazzle our thinking to harm us. Instead, our brains flood as an automatic reflex designed to put our bodies into an emergency state to protect us. One of our primary defense mechanisms that has kept us alive for thousands of years has been that our amygdalae and emotional system will commandeer our frontal lobes, or the brain's executive center, and give ultimate control to our much faster emotional and fight-or-flight system. This shift in control from our frontal lobes to our emotional and fight-or-flight systems puts us on "automatic" so we can react at lightning speed to keep us safe. The logical, methodical, and more accurate thinking brain, or our frontal lobes, takes a back seat to the much faster but less accurate emotional and fight-or-flight systems.

So, we are plunged into "**cognitive dysfunction**."[70]

If these stressful conditions are allowed to continue and the adrenaline and cortisol are allowed to routinely flood our brains, the dendrites and axons of the hippocampus will become damaged. Over time, continued flooding of the dendrites and axons in our hippocampus will cause them to atrophy and die. Eventually, this **hippocampal atrophy** can become so bad it can even be seen on an MRI.[71]

As a result, the hippocampus will no longer be able to fire electronically and catch the chemical messages that comprise our short-term working memory. Quite frankly, we lose much of our short-term memory because we have burned off the dendrites and axons in our hippocampus, so we simply don't have enough "fingers" to catch or send our thoughts.

Think of it this way. Most of us could catch a ball if it was thrown to us. We would hold up our hands, flex our fingers, and catch the ball. That would be easy for most of us.

But what if we cut off your fingers? How easy would it be to catch the ball now? It would be almost impossible. Over time, flooding destroys the dendrites and axons in your hippocampus, so our short-term memory gets worse.

I will often ask the attendees at my seminars how many of them would like to retire and travel one day. At least half of the people in the room will raise their hands.

I then ask them how many of them would want to retire and travel and know what city they're in?

Make no mistake: There is no reason you cannot maintain your short-term memory for your entire life. There aren't any moving parts in your brain. Elbows wear out. Knees wear out. They are mechanical. However, everything in your brain is chemical and electrical. You cannot wear your brain out, but you can burn it out—very easily.

The neurons in our brains actually have an average life expectancy of **120 years**, which is way beyond the current expected life span of any human. However, since most of us treat our brains like soccer balls, many of us start losing our short-term memory function at about the age of 40 or 50 years old, which is not even half of our neurons' life expectancy. As a result, most of us lose our mental capacities decades before their time.[72]

So, why do we lose our short-term memory but keep our long-term memories? Because most of our long-term memory is stored way up in the outside and back of our brain in areas such as the neocortex, which is the brain's wrinkly-looking outer layer—far away from these chemical hurricanes.

The solution: maximize your eustress chemicals and minimize the distress.

## HEALTH RISK #5: MENTAL IMPAIRMENTS

Another important point to consider regarding the flooding of adrenaline and cortisol in our brains and bodies is our mental health. Again, it is so obvious that it evades us:

> **Everything we think, how we think, and how we relate to others is controlled by our brain.**

Unfortunately, far too many of us still think of our "mind" and our "body" as being separate from one another. They are not.

Your brain is involved in **everything** you do. If your brain does not work right, then you will not work right—which is the way you feel and behave toward others. However, if you continue to flood your brain with toxic levels of adrenaline and cortisol, you will burn and damage your brain. We call this a "mental impairment."

Think of it this way. What if you went home every night and soaked your feet in one of those little whirlpool baths? That would feel great and it would be very good for your feet.

But what if you filled the whirlpool with gasoline? And what if you did this every day for one hour? What would this do to your feet?

Then, what if you did this every day for one hour for five years? Ten years? Fifteen years? What would happen to your feet?

When you continually flood your brain with massive amounts of adrenaline and cortisol . . .

> **What do you think you are doing to your brain?**

Still, we do not think of our brains as controlling our mental health, which only reinforces the stigmas surrounding mental disorders. That is why humans will readily admit that they have at one time or another injured their leg, sprained their wrist and so on. But with mental disorders, we somehow think they are different. We do not think of mental impairments as being related to any physical damage to our brain.

This is why you probably won't see someone wearing a shirt that says, "Bipolar and Proud!"

Consequently, we humans go into denial with problems related to our mental health, which only makes everything worse because you are not only denying yourself the eustress chemicals you would get by feeling the support from others, but you are subjecting yourself to even more distress worrying over who knows about it and who will find out.

But if you think about it, this is all very illogical. What makes you think that you can injure your heart but you cannot injure your brain—the most fragile organ in your body?

Again, even though your brain only comprises about 2% to 3% of the average person's body weight, it burns 25% of everything we consume, it uses 25% of our blood flow, and 20% of all the oxygen we breathe, which also contributes to why our brain is typically the first organ to be damaged when we subject it to chronic distress, smoking, a bad diet, toxic fumes and so on.[73]

Unfortunately, for humans, we are not wired to focus on the positive things in our lives. Instead, we are wired to go right to the negative, which today does nothing but needlessly skyrocket our level of anxiety.

The reason for this phenomenon is simple. When we were all wandering around here 5,000-plus years ago, the world was a very dangerous place. At any second, we could easily end up as lunch for some predator. So, it was better to go to the negative than to the positive.

For instance, if we saw something off in the distance, it was safer for us to assume it was a lion. It might be a rock, but if we were wrong about that, the mistake could be fatal. So, it was always safer to go to the negative and assume it was a lion.[74]

If our ancestors didn't think that way, you probably wouldn't be here right now reading this book.

We call this "negativity bias." We humans will most always focus on the negative aspects of someone first, which is why it is so easy to destroy one's own reputation. We see this happen all the time, such as with President Bill Clinton. No matter what he accomplished during his eight years as President, he will always be remembered for the "blue dress" and Monica Lewinsky.[75]

In Rick Hanson's book, *Buddha's Brain*, he describes the human brain as being "Velcro for bad experiences and Teflon for good."

> **Therefore, we humans are not wired to be happy. We are wired to stay alive.**

In my last book, *Living The Five Skills of Tolerance*, I described a wonderful scene where it is a beautiful day and you are standing out in a lush green meadow. In the distance, you see a unicorn running free. Yes, you actually see a real, live unicorn playing out in the field. All you can think about is getting a picture to sell to a national tabloid. You are going to be rich!

At that second, a hungry bear comes running out of the woods towards you. You instantly run for the car and barely make it inside when the bear crashes into it.

Once you get home and see your family, what will you tell everyone about first? It will be the bear. It almost ate you! Even though you saw a mythological unicorn, you will be consumed with the fact that you were almost eaten by a common everyday bear. But that is how we humans are programmed: to focus on the negative.

Yes, your brain sends you negative thoughts all the time. It lies to you.[76]

This is what Dr. Daniel Amen calls "ANTs," or automatic negative thoughts. I have these all the time, just like everyone else, so I coach myself whenever it happens. I remember running to catch a connector flight from Chicago back home to Columbus, Ohio. I had to run from one terminal to another because the information the airline gave me was flat wrong. Luckily, I made my flight with two minutes to spare.

As I sat in my seat, I remember thinking how mad I was at the airline. If I had been given the correct information, I wouldn't have had any trouble at all catching my flight. Since I was presenting at 9:00 am the next morning, had I missed my flight, I would have had to rent a car, then make the six-hour drive to Columbus. I could feel myself getting more and more angry as I reflected on what almost happened.

So, I took a deep breath, slowed down my thinking, and told myself, "That is not real. It is an ANT. It isn't going to hurt you. That bad thing didn't happen to you, even though it was close. You are on the plane and will be home in 45 minutes. Your anger is not real. Let it go. It doesn't matter. This is your inner Fred Flintstone trying to hurt you."

Today, ANTs will do nothing but make our anxiety levels soar, which will flood and damage our brains. Knowing that you are a caveman or cavewoman wired to automatically react to the negative can give you that added incentive to slow down and think.

> **REMEMBER:**
>
> **Unless your life really is in danger, your first reaction to a conflict is always wrong.**

This also happens whenever we see or think of someone who has bullied us. We instantly become infested with ANTs. This is why every time we see or think about a troll, we get that sick and tight feeling in our stomach, which are our adrenal glands starting to flood our bodies. Our amygdalae are putting us on "high alert," which makes us "hypervigilant" toward these people. Our brain thinks this person is threatening us, regardless of whether that person is there or not.

This is how trolls cause mental impairments in both themselves and in those around them: flooding.

Again, you can actually contract a mental impairment in different ways. You could be born with one. You could also have an injury or an illness that would damage your brain. Your diet could give you a mental impairment, which will be discussed in more detail later in this book. However, more than any of these single factors, it is the people around you that can **literally** drive you crazy by causing you to continuously flood and burn various parts of your brain. For most of us, that is the greatest threat to our health.

Perhaps few individuals are suffering more from the horrendous effects of chronic distress than our service men and women. Our military personnel are suffering from a host of mental issues, many of which are ending in suicide. According to the USO, suicides in the United States military are at an all-time high. Four times as many service men and women are committing suicide than were killed in combat in the last 20 years.[77]

As another example, over three-quarters of all the state, county and municipal retirees in Ohio are on some psychotropic medication, such as antidepressants, according to the Ohio Public Employees Retirement System. That is true in most states. Now, think about that. You have worked your whole life to enjoy your retirement years only to spend them battling a mental illness and taking psychiatric medications for the rest of your life. That is a tragedy.

Surrounding ourselves with emotionally intelligent people keeps us healthy and productive. It is essential that we work and live in SAFE environments. Working and living with trolls kills not only our productivity, but it kills us as well—literally.

So, does this mean that one bad apple can ruin the whole barrel? **ABSOLUTELY!** This constant flooding we experience by working with bullies will actually change how our brain functions.

In the end, bullies, or trolls, make you sick in many ways. Why we let these trolls stay and torture our good people I will **never** understand.

So, let's move on to the more positive parts of this book, which begins with rewiring your brain.

# 5

## REWIRING YOUR BRAIN

### SOCIAL EPIGENETICS

Remember. It is so obvious that it evades us:

> *Everything*—ABSOLUTELY
> EVERYTHING—that happens in our
> brain is chemical and electrical.

Social epigenetics is the study of how the neurons in our brains change in response to the outside world. Yes, the cells in our brains physically change in response to our everyday experiences.

Modern science has discovered that one factor which causes our brain cells to alter themselves involves the "methyl" molecule. The methyl molecule not only determines whether certain genes will be "turned on or off," but it also determines how far their activity levels will be "turned up" or "turned down." It is the methyl molecule that determines where over 100 billion neurons in the brain will end up, and which neurons will connect to one another. The methyl molecule directly sculpts not only our bodies, but also the neurons in our brains.[78]

Therefore, thanks to social epigenetics, the century-old debate of "nature versus nurture" has been settled:

**Nurture *IS* Nature.**

Therefore, even though our genes may predispose us to certain conditions, the environment we subject these neurons to will play a big role in how they form and which ones will be activated. Both our genes *and* our experiences determine who we will become, which includes how our brains will form throughout our entire lives. We now know that our genes and our environment are *not* independent of each other. Instead, they are interdependent.[79]

Simply being born with a certain set of genes or neurons is not the final determination of who we will become. Again, we turn on and turn off these genes by virtue of how we live, which includes what we eat, who we associate with, our exercise habits, and so on.

For example, the food we eat contains hundreds of minerals, vitamins, and other substances that regulate our genes. If we eat the wrong foods, over time we can activate those genes that will cause our arteries to clog and give us heart disease.

But if we eat more vegetables filled with the vitamins and minerals that are good for us, then we will feed those genes that will work to keep us healthy. The same is true for our brains. Eating the right foods and associating with the right people will allow us to wire our brains to have more stable moods and better dispositions. This, of course, gives us a healthier brain and a higher level of emotional intelligence.

Today, we know that it is biologically *impossible* for genes to operate independently of their environment. Our genes were actually designed to be influenced and regulated by the signals they receive from the environment we expose them to, which includes the combination of neurotransmitters in our brains. One of the greatest factors influencing the chemical balance existing in our brains comes from our daily and ongoing social interactions, as we saw with the people living in Roseto, Pennsylvania. Therefore, the interactions we have with others has a profound influence on how our brain develops throughout our lives.

According to Dr. John C. Crabbe, Senior Research Career Scientist at the Virginia Medical Center and Professor of Behavioral Neuroscience:

> "Social epigenetics is part of the next frontier in genomics ... The new technical challenge involves factoring in the impact of the environment on differences in gene expression. It's another blow against the naïve view of genetic determinism: that our experiences don't matter – that genes are all."

We now know that every social interaction we have "reshapes" our brain due to the chemical flow and the electrical charge generated by our thoughts. This reshaping of our brain is called "neuroplasticity".

Dr. Ronald Siegel, Psy.D. of Harvard Medical School refers to neuroplasticity as "Experience Based Neuroplasticity." Debbie Hampton, author of *Beat Depression And Anxiety By Changing Your Brain,* refers to our brains and neuroplasticity as the "Play-Doh in our heads." Both are very accurate descriptions of how vulnerable our brains are to the environment around us.

# NEUROPLASTICITY: NEURONS, DENDRITES, & SYNAPSES

Our neurons are the actual cells that grow and form our brains and our autonomic nervous system, or ANS, which runs throughout our entire body. The dendrites and axons in our brains connect our neurons to one another.

## NEURONS

Understanding how neurons work is actually simple. First, our neurons are the only cells in our bodies that communicate with one another. Although we have trillions of other cells in our body, none of them actually communicate with one another except for our neurons.

### How Neurons Communicate or "Fire"

**Dendrites** ••••▶ **Axons**

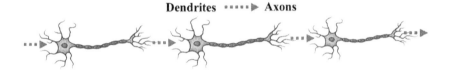

However, our neurons never touch one another, which is actually an engineering marvel. Instead, an electrical charge enters the neuron through its dendrites. The charge then travels through the body of the neuron and exits through the bottom at the axon, which is where the charge is then sent onto another neuron entering through its dendrites, and so on, and so on.[80]

Since these neurons never touch one another, the electrical charge transferred between them has to "jump" from the axon, which is the sender of the message, to the dendrite, which is the receiver. For the electrical charge to make this jump from the axon to the dendrite, neurotransmitters are "fired" out from the axon. We call the spaces or gaps between the dendrites and the axons "synapses," which I will refer to as "connections." It is across these connections where our neurons communicate with one another.[81]

To keep the speed at which our thoughts travel in perspective, these signals fire from neuron to neuron at 268 miles per hour—which is faster than the stock cars at the Indianapolis 500.[82]

## SYNAPSES BETWEEN AXONS AND DENDRITES

The message the neurons are trying to send to each other are contained inside the neurotransmitters. So, for us to think clearly, we must always have a ready supply of fresh neurotransmitters on hand.

Our neurotransmitters are stored and then fired out from one neuron to the other and then back and forth, as shown in the following graphic.[83]

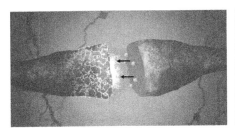 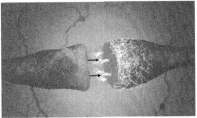

## UNDERSTANDING NEUROPLASTY

Neuroscientists refer to our brains as being "plastic," which means our brains can change shape in response to their need to become more efficient. Since our brains have the physical consistency of soft butter, the brain's neurons can change their shape in response to their environment and the demands we place on them. That means we can actually rewire our brain.[84]

Neuroplasticity is why therapy works for stroke victims. The therapies a stroke victim will go through involve repetitive motions, so the neurons in that area of the brain where the damage occurred are forced to fire with one another and grow. The damaged neurons are most likely not going to repair themselves. Instead, the healthy neurons surrounding that area of the brain will grow into the damaged area and rewire it with new connections.

That is why Michael's Interactive Metronome therapy helped him increase his coordination by 800%. All the time he was doing this, he was growing new neurons and generating new sprouts from his existing neurons already living in his cerebellum. That is why his 2008 SPECT brain scans showed that his cerebellum was burning much fuller than it was in 2006.

Rewiring and building up his cerebellum gave him the increased coordination to run track, which helped him build up his body and develop his neurons to where many other parts of his brain could also rewire and improve.

It truly is momentum. Michael used the Interactive Metronome to rewire his cerebellum and therefore his coordination. I don't know how much progress he could have made in the other areas of his brain if he had not developed his cerebellum. Activity is a key factor in neuroplasticity.

And don't forget: The cerebellum governs our organizational skills. I don't know how well he would have done in college if he was still relying on his "organized chaos" system for arranging his schoolwork.

Again, we call such therapies CBT, which stands for "cognitive behavioral therapy." In reality, it is rewiring the brain.

Neuroplasticity, or the reshaping of our neurons, occurs whenever our dendrites and axons "fire" and messages are transmitted between neurons. As we repeat our experiences, thoughts, or actions again and again, these neurons continuously fire with electricity, which causes dendrites and axons to actually "melt" or be "re-sculpted." The more we repeat the same actions or thoughts, the more those specific neurons in our brains will fire, melt, and reshape themselves.

Think of it this way: What would happen if you took an electric wire and sent an electrical charge through soft room temperature butter? It would melt, right? Well, that is what happens to the dendrites and axons in your brain when they are hit with an electrical charge. They melt and conform to one another.

When we repeat our actions, such as when we practice hitting a baseball again and again and again, what we are actually doing is changing the shape, size, and configuration of the neurons in our brain into something new, as well as growing new connections. The more we use these neurons, the more they conform to one another and the more efficient they become in transmitting the chemical messages that travel between them. Yes, repeated activity reshapes the neurons in our brain.

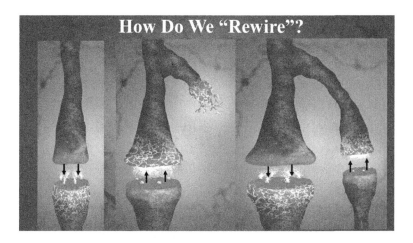

**NEUROPLASTICITY: DIFFERENT SHAPES OF DENDRITES**

In this graphic, you will see examples of three shapes of neurons. The ones on the far left are young and have not been used very much. So, they are long, thin, and not very efficient in transferring neurotransmitters back and forth between the dendrite and the axon since their shapes have not conformed to each other yet.[85]

However, the more this person actually uses these neurons, the electrical charges shooting back and forth between the neurons will actually cause them to melt so they can begin conforming to one another. That will flatten out the surface area between the two, which will allow them to communicate much more efficiently. That is what is happening with the neurons in the middle graphic.

As this person uses and fires these neurons more and more, the electrical charge will overload the neuron to where another new sprout will begin to grow. You can see this happening in the middle graphic.

In the far-right graphic, you will see that the original dendrite and axon are working very efficiently and have fully conformed to one another. You can see that the new young sprout is also firing with another neuron. Soon, it will also flatten out and then have additional sprouts of its own, if the person keeps using them.

Neuroplasticity is one reason the old adage is correct: **"Practice makes perfect."**

This is also why there is really no such thing as "muscle memory." It is "brain memory," which is what you are really building the more you practice something.

This also explains why people who have had a limb amputated feel phantom pains. Logically, we know that part of the body has been removed, but the area of the brain that controlled the amputated limb does not know it. So, the brain continues to send signals to that body part just like it was still connected.[86]

This is also why concert violinists and pianists have so many more synapses in the hand and finger coordination areas of their brains than the rest of us. They have practiced their craft so many times that they have actually rewired their brains and added millions of new axons and dendrites to the area of their brains that control their hand and finger coordination. They literally could play their instruments in their sleep.[87]

These newly developed connections are often called "Hebbian Synapses," after the great Canadian psychologist, Donald Hebb. Hebb has been described as the father of neuropsychology and neural networks due to his research into neurons working in tandem with one another.

Hebb theorized that neurons are strengthened the more they fire and interact with one another. This constant and repetitive firing causes the neurons to not only conform their shape to one another, which makes them more efficient, but even more sprouts are formed, strengthening the neurons' bonds to each other even further.

> **THIS IS HOW HUMANS DEVELOP HABITS.**

Today, this phenomenon is called "Hebb's Law," which is often paraphrased as, "Neurons that fire together wire together."

## "NEUROGENESIS" and "SYNAPTOGENESIS"

Yes, our neurons will actually change their shape to operate more efficiently with one another the more they are used, and they also will grow more connections or sprouts. This growth of new sprouts is called "synaptogenesis," which means we are creating new synapses, or connections, between the existing neurons all the time. Scientists actually believe that growing new connections keeps happening right up until we die.[88]

Besides reshaping the neurons that already exist in our brains and growing new connections, we also grow brand new neurons every month. We used to think that humans were born with all the neurons they would ever have, but that is not true. We now know that the brain and spinal cord contain stem cells that grow into thousands of new neurons every day.[89]

Recent studies by Fernando Nottebohm and Bruce McEwen, neuroscientists at Rockefeller University, have shown that humans continue to generate new neurons throughout their lives. So, when our brain grows new neurons from stem cells in our brains, we call this "neurogenesis."[90]

Neurogenesis continues in our brains well into old age, although it slows down considerably as we get older. However, engaging in physically and mentally challenging activities stimulates neurogenesis.

Interestingly enough, the vast majority of new cell growth occurs in the hippocampus. As discussed earlier, our hippocampus, which is located right behind the amygdalae, is the primary system we use for learning new information. We use our hippocampus to recall what we have just recently learned, which we call "working memory." This is the neural process we go through when we learn.

As you now know, every thought we have reconstructs our brain just a little bit. Therefore, it is crucial that we make good choices regarding who we choose for friends and the relationships we maintain in our lives for one simple reason:

> **What we think and how we think will eventually make us who we will become—LITERALLY.**[91]

# BUILDING SKILLS: USING NEUROGENESIS AND NEUROPLASTICITY TO "REWIRE" OURSELVES

Due to the fact that we humans really can rewire our brains, CBT, or cognitive behavioral therapy, works. If we humans slow down our thought processes and use our frontal lobes, or our logical brain, we can learn to master many of our emotional reactions by rewiring our neurons.

For instance, if someone can logically reason their way through their fears or "sensitive spots," and then logically play out what bothers them or scares them again and again in their minds, and then expose themselves to such situations in a controlled manner, those people can rewire themselves so they can learn to control their emotional reactions when the threatening situation arises for real. Eventually, we can face what we find most disturbing or what frightens us without feeling overwhelmed with emotion. This is commonly called "exposure therapy."

According to Dr. Joseph LeDoux, we can actually rewire the cells in our brain to gain better control over our emotions and our fight-or-flight response.

For example, Dr. LeDoux tells of a New York City traffic officer who had gone into a full-blown rage when a motorist called her a "low-life bitch." Rather than risk losing her temper again, and possibly her job, she went to therapy. In her sessions, that phrase was repeated to her again and again, first in a flat tone, then with increasing emotional intensity, and finally with obscene gestures added into the mix. After she had been exposed to this phrase and abuse several times and did not react, she later stayed calm in the face of such insults when she encountered them in the real world.

So, how was this done? The police officer basically rewired her emotional and fight-or-flight systems.

Psychotherapy is a learning process for patients, which means it is a way to rewire the brain.[92]

Dr. LeDoux says, "It's something like what happens naturally when we churn a worry over in our mind, and come to a new perspective." Yes, humans can consciously use their logical brain to rewire themselves, which is what we commonly call a "habit."

Think of it this way. What if we all started jogging and we did this at 3:00 am? At first, that would be painful, wouldn't it? Many of us would probably just turn off the alarm clock and go back to sleep.

However, some of us would get up and go jogging. It would be painful, but we would do it.

But think about this: What will happen in three months... four months... six months? Won't many of us just wake up at 3:00 am on our own without the alarm clock? We would because we have rewired our brains. We have literally constructed new neural pathways in our brains to where we now just "automatically" react, or wake up, at 3:00 am.

We have just formed a habit, which is really a rewiring of the brain.

This is also why so many of us drive to work each day and don't have a clue how we got there.

Another way to think about rewiring our brain is to think of a fresh blanket of snow on the ground. At first, you cannot see the street or the sidewalk. But when the first person walks through the snow and onto the sidewalk, a slight path is formed. If no other people follow this trail, then it will simply blow away and disappear. However, as more people follow the footsteps laid down by the first person who walked through the snow, the path becomes more pronounced. It becomes stronger and stronger until eventually it becomes a vivid pathway that is easy to follow.[93]

That is how the circuitry in our brain works to form habits and to develop skills. The first neural circuitry connections we make initially are weak. However, as we repeat the process again and again, the neural circuits become stronger every time we repeat this process until eventually these neural pathways become so strong that our behavior becomes automatic. We then instinctively follow this new neural circuit.

Your brain was constructed during childhood because of many genetic influences **and** the environment you were exposed to at that time. Your DNA dictated that you would be given certain neurons and it dictated where they would be located. However, through the experiences you had with the outside world, your diet and other factors, your connections have been adjusted and rewired, which further sculpted your brain into its own unique pattern. Millions of the connections in your brain have been adjusted by your environment, which now drives how your neurons react to different situations.

When we have these experiences in life, we call it "learning." In reality, the line between neural plasticity and learning is nonexistent. Learning **IS** neuroplasticity.

## NAVY SEALS: REWIRING YOUR BRAIN TO CONTROL FEAR

We now know we can rewire our brains to where our logical brain can actually gain control of a human being's most primal emotional reaction: **fear.**

In the History Channel's special, *The Brain*, researchers took an in-depth look at how fear, the brain's primary and most powerful emotional response, can be controlled.

Researchers studied the training and dropout rate of Navy Seals, who undergo one of the most rigorous military training programs in the world. The Navy Seal program is so demanding that only 25% of the recruits, some of whom are former Olympic athletes, can pass the training. It is an honor to just be given the opportunity to participate in this training. Only a hand-selected few are even permitted to enroll. Therefore, even among this elite class of recruits whom the military thought would make good candidates for this program, only 25% can call themselves Navy Seals in the end.

What makes the Navy Seal training so difficult and sets it apart from many other military programs are not the physical requirements, but rather the mental demands placed upon its recruits. In the final test for the potential Navy Seals, the recruit is forced to confront a human's greatest natural fear: drowning.

In this final test, the recruits jump into a pool of water with their air tanks and they are expected to remain submerged for 20 minutes. However, while the recruits are under water, their instructor comes over to them and pulls out their air hose and ties it into knots. If the recruits panic, they will gasp for air and must return to the surface.

This is when the recruits usually fail.

The recruits are expected to keep their cool and calmly take the hose, untie the knot, put the hose back into their mouth, and breathe more air. However, about the same time the recruits get a few precious gulps of air, another instructor comes up from behind them and takes out the hose again.

Again, the recruits must control their primal urge to panic and rush back to the surface.

This goes on again and again for 20 minutes.

Anyone who has ever been in a pool and accidentally taken a gulp of water can attest to how horrific this experience is.

However, the Navy wondered if there was a way for those recruits who were close to passing, yet failed, to gain better control over their emotional response to the fear of drowning, and complete this final test.

What the Navy did was remarkably simple yet neurologically brilliant.

The Navy began training its recruits in a four-step "Seal Mental Toughness Program," which includes:

1. **Goal Setting**

   The Navy Seal recruits established their goals for every test in the program, and actually recorded these goals in writing.

   This act of actually setting specific goals and writing them down helps the recruits' frontal lobes become more focused and gain a sense of control over the chaos that usually allows the amygdalae to dominante their actions. Goal setting was found to help bring order to this confusion, which helped to keep their amygdalae in check.

2. **Visualization or "Mental Rehearsal"**

   The Navy Seal recruits would repeatedly practice staying calm in their minds and meditating while imagining themselves being underwater with their instructors pulling the air tubes out of their mouths and tying it into knots. They then imagined themselves calmly untying the air hose and returning it to their mouths, then calmly breathing once again.

   Again, this meditation and imagery allowed the recruits to rewire their brains to where their frontal lobes could gain better control over their fight-or-flight response and their emotions.

3. **Self-Talk**

   The Navy Seal recruits also talk themselves through the entire underwater exercise out loud, not just in their heads.

Since our minds can race through several thoughts in just a few seconds, speaking is a much slower and more thoughtful process, since we can speak only a few hundred words per minute. Therefore, coaching or talking to yourself will slow your brain and thoughts down to where your frontal lobes can gain much better control of your emotions and your fight-or-flight response, organize your thoughts, reason through them, and ultimately control them.

Yes, self-talk can actually override our emotional and fight-or-flight systems.

4. **Arousal Control**

The Navy Seal recruits would also meditate to slow down their breathing. They would take deep breaths, then slowly exhale, which allows more oxygen to get into the brain. With increased oxygen in the body and the brain in this meditative state, the heart slows and the brain calms down, except for the frontal lobes. Brain imaging has shown us that while meditation calms other parts of the brain, it actually results in increased activity in our frontal lobes. Clearly, this helps us concentrate much better, which results in more emotional control.

With the recruits gaining much better control over their emotions, the Navy Seal pass rate went from 25% to 33%.

In short, humans can retrain, or rewire, their brains to gain better emotional control. This realization has changed the way our military trains Navy Seals.

If such rewiring can help a Navy Seal deal with the fear of drowning, think what it could do for what you are dealing with in your life.

# 6

## HEALING YOUR BRAIN

By now, you should have a much better understanding of how devastating the effects of chronic distress are for all of us and how beneficial and healing the effects of eustress can be. You should also have a very good understanding of how the brain works, how we damage it, and how we can better enable our bodies to repair and rewire it.

With that, it is time to look at what Michael and I did to repair our brains. You should now better understand why we did what we did and continue to do to this day.

There is not just one thing you need to do to get a healthier brain. Instead, there are many daily lifestyle choices you will need to make, and most of them you will probably like. However, it is important not to overwhelm yourself. It is a lot like starting at the gym. If you spend two hours working out initially, you will be too sore to go back. I always tell my seminar attendees and clients to pick **three things** from what we will talk about and start with those. Some are easier to do than others. Then, once those things become habits, start another, then another, and then another.

> **Brain and body health is a marathon,
> not a sprint.**

Also, neurons grow slower than any other cells in the body. That means you need to be patient but diligent. Don't give up. You didn't damage your brain overnight, and it will take a while to repair. But stick with it.

Not everything Michael and I did will be right for everyone. We don't even follow the same routines. Michael is a long-distance runner. I hate the impact, so I would rather use a glider. Michael eats beets and likes his salads without any dressing. I would rather eat my shoe. So, I find other things that work for me.

Again, my program consisted of:

1. Get as many jackasses out of my life as possible.
2. Get my physical and fasting blood work.
3. Focus on positive thoughts, friends, and pets.
4. Enjoy my hobbies, such as photography.
5. Engage in a meditation routine.
6. Adopt a new diet lifestyle.
7. Maintain a regimen of vitamin and mineral supplements.
8. Water: Drink half my weight in ounces every day.
9. Get enough sleep.
10. Adopt an aerobic exercise, strength training and sex program.
11. Get monthly massages.
12. You need to design and plan your own program and live it.

As you will notice, several of these various aspects of my program are really outlets for my distress. I am trying to displace my distress chemicals with more eustress chemicals. Having many different outlets in your life are critical to displace your distress with eustress.

With that said, let's get started.

## Get As Many Jackasses Out Of Your Life As Possible

This is not easy to do, but it is a big one.

Bullies, trolls, and jackasses are caustic to your life. They will kill you. They can easily be your number-one health risk.

We all have to deal with bullies who make our guts churn. That is just part of life. However, there are also certain people in our lives who we really don't have to keep seeing. Some people can be excised, and sometimes they are relatives. We all need to take a serious look at who causes us distress, and, if at all possible, get rid of them.

When I first got my brain scanned back in 2008, I took a real hard look at who was causing me grief. Sometimes they were certain clients. So, I dropped them. They just were not worth the adrenaline and cortisol.

We can all do that. Unless someone is absolutely essential to your world, if they are a troll, excise them. You need to ask yourself, "Is this person worth the cost of the second-hand smoke they are giving to me?" If the answer is no, get rid of them.

I also took a page from "Johnny the Bagger" and wanted to get as much Flow as I could into my work. I stopped taking certain projects I hated and I leaned into those that I loved doing. I got more and more creative with my presentations and the graphics I used in my programs. It all made my daily life better.

Work life is key in making this determination. If you work somewhere that makes you sick to your stomach Sunday night over the thought of going back into that hell hole on Monday, you need to look at making a change. Yes, in many cases, finding another job might be the most brain healthy move you can make.

If you are an employer or supervisor reading this book, then you really need to take a hard look at the environment you are creating, not just for your employees, but for your own sake as well.

The bottom line is simple:

> **To attract and retain employees in the twenty-first century, and in order to create and maintain healthy workplaces, we need to create environments that are SAFE.**

Today's world is becoming more and more intolerant. That means it is not safe to voice your opinion or to disagree with someone else. As the world becomes more and more diverse, we often find ourselves surrounded by people whose ideas differ from ours. This could be a good thing, but not if someone is going to attack you for having a different point of view. It is often worse if that person is a Retreater, or a passive aggressive bully, who stabs you in the back later for disagreeing with their illustrious opinion. This happens all the time, such as when it comes to talking about vaccinations, gun control, management decisions, and so on. Walking on eggshells like that will keep us in a constant state of distress. Since we all spend so many of our waking hours at work, how we spend those hours is critical to our health.

REMEMBER: Whatever happens in the world today will be in your workplace tomorrow—if not this afternoon. It is unavoidable. If you do not create and enforce an environment where it is safe to disagree, then you are doomed. (Now you can see a big reason why most everyone you know is on psychiatric medication.)

If you want to see a model for the environment you want to create, re-read the earlier section on Roseto.

Unfortunately, how the vast majority of workplaces operate in America is horrendous:

- According to the *New York Daily News*, about 70% of American workers are miserable at work.[94]
- *Staff Squared* reports that 85% of employees hate their jobs.[95]
- Gallup Poll reported that only 30% of all American workers are engaged when they go to work every day. Gallup also reported that the way we manage employees today is 30 years out of date.[96]
- And, under normal conditions, according to OSHA (the U.S. Occupational Safety and Health Administration) there are over 38,000 physical assaults that occur every week in American workplaces and we average about two homicides every workday.[97]

Since 2007, the Harris Poll has conducted its "Stress in America" survey on behalf of the American Psychological Association, or the APA. The APA has seen various external factors negatively affect our distress levels, such as economic downturns, racism, and political conflict. However, the survey has consistently reported that the two greatest stressors in our lives are either "financial" or "work life." In various years, these two culprits rotated for the top spot, with the other coming in second. However, this all makes sense: Both factors directly affect our very survival.[98]

Of course, when people are reporting work life as being the number-one stressor in their lives, they are referring to the bullies.

However, the 2020 survey was different. It revealed that Americans have been profoundly affected by the COVID-19 pandemic, even though such external factors as money, work life, and even racism continued to be significant sources of distress. These factors are now compounding the distress we are all experiencing, which is having serious consequences on our minds and bodies.[99]

The APA is sounding the alarm. It is telling us:

> **We are facing a national mental health crisis that could yield serious health and social consequences for years to come.**

The APA says we have to act right now to help those who need it, and to prevent a much more serious and widespread mental health crisis.[100]

As you know, the chronic distress we get from bullies is one of the worst forms of flooding our body can experience. It is three times worse than impersonal stressors. The last thing we all need today is more bullying on top of everything else that is happening.

Unfortunately, we are not getting better at dealing with our bullies—we are getting worse. On December 29, 2021, Bruce Shutan published his article, "Workplace bullying: A 'wildly out of control' epidemic" on hrexecutive.com. In this article, he wrote:

"Despite calls for understanding and compassion over COVID-19's massive disruption and an ensuing trend toward empathetic leadership, there's just no escaping **meanness**: As many as 75% of employees report that they have been a target of or have witnessed bullying at work, which has affected an estimated 79.3 million U.S. workers, according to the Workplace Bullying Institute."

Every organization must strive to attain and maintain a safe environment. That means:

- Is the workplace safe from germs?
- Will I go home with all my fingers and toes?
- Is it safe to be different, like being Black, White, male, female, gay, disabled, and so on?
- Is it safe to disagree with other people?
- Is it safe to disagree with my boss?

> **That is how we define TRUST: Is it SAFE?**

If not, then the organization will become toxic and disaster will follow in the form of employment lawsuits, low morale, high turnover, and, yes, workplace violence, all of which are out of control today.

If you do not work in a SAFE environment, then make it safe or find another one.

If you are the employer and you run an UNSAFE workplace, then change it.

Now you know why this is the third book in my trilogy. My first book addressed emotional intelligence and conflict resolution, or EPR, which stands for Empathic Listening, Parroting, and "Rewards." My second book focused on being more tolerant. So, if you don't do what is in those first two books, as most of us have not, you will need this book to understand how to get your brain back.

## Physical Health Examination and Full Fasting Blood Work

To properly care for your brain, it is important for you to go see your physician and check on your overall health. People who have trouble controlling themselves in conflict situations are often having some type of health issues. Diabetes, thyroid conditions, menopause, low-T, and a host of other issues can easily upset the hormonal balance in your body and therefore the chemical balance in your blood.

Millions of Americans are walking around with diabetes and don't have a clue they have it. However, the excess glucose in their blood stream could easily present itself as "depression," "anxiety," "anger," and so on. I have had several clients who have been on various types of psychotropic medications only to discover their real problem was diabetes or a thyroid condition.

I was one of those people. My physicians put me on various types of medications for depression because of the symptoms I was exhibiting when I turned 50. Amazingly, they put me on antidepressants without even testing my blood sugar. In fact, my doctor gave me a sucker to cheer me up at the end of our appointment.

I had diabetes, not depression, even though the symptoms were identical.

So, when the antidepressants did not work, my psychiatrist upped my dosage. Instead of checking my blood for what other conditions might have been causing my emotional mood swings, my doctors simply filled me full of psychotropic medications. And in case you didn't know, antidepressants **do not** help you at all with your diabetes. That is why you should **always** insist on having a full fasting blood test before your doctor whips out their prescription pad like Marshall Dillon.

Also, when you are having your fasting blood test performed, check your vitamin D levels. Since vitamin D helps make your cells more receptive to insulin, which allows the glucose to enter your cells more easily, low levels of vitamin D may indicate that you are more prone to contracting Type 2 diabetes. Everyone should know the level of vitamin D in their system. Unfortunately, checking your vitamin D level is not part of many standard blood tests. You need to ask your physician to add it to the order.

I've had clients in trouble at work for being "too difficult" with their coworkers. When I sent them for a full physical and a fasting blood test, we actually discovered that they had a thyroid problem or were pre-menopausal, which threw off their hormone levels and affected their behavior. Rather than getting fired or going into therapy, they corrected the physical problem, which then corrected the brain functioning problem, and with it their level of emotional intelligence and their ability to build relationships.

If a woman's level of progesterone drops, which is very common in menopause, the body loses its natural "sleeping pill" and anti-anxiety hormone. Low progesterone can cause headaches, migraines, mood swings, and difficulty thinking and focusing. Those of you old enough to remember, just think of Edith Bunker going through "the change."

Progesterone is a "feel good" hormone, much like Xanax. It helps calm us down.[101]

And don't forget the effects of male menopause, which includes a drop in the body's level of testosterone. When our testosterone level drops, the blood flow to the brain also drops. This poses a great threat to the health of the brain. Also, research now links low levels of testosterone to Alzheimer's disease. These facts more than motivated me to get my own blood levels checked every year.

This is also why sending employees to "anger management" rarely works. It is hard to control your temper when you have a damaged brain that is "on fire," or when it is being deprived of much needed blood or nutrients or when your hormone levels are out of balance. Heal the brain—**then** change the behavior.

> **Think of it this way: If your hormone or blood levels were off, you'd be grouchy too.**

You also want to make sure you thoroughly check out how your thyroid is working, which is often overlooked in fasting blood tests. In the human body, the thalamus is what gives direction to our thyroid to regulate many of our hormones, which includes our adrenaline and insulin, so it is the great regulator of our blood sugar levels. If your thyroid works too slowly, which we call being "hypothyroid," then you can feel depressed, irritable, and have trouble concentrating.

But if your thyroid works too fast, which we call "hyperthyroid," then you can feel jittery, anxious, irritable, and overheated.

This is why many of the "problem people" I have coached were being treated for depression, anxiety, and a host of other mental impairments. However, when I sent them to get a full physical, the reality of the situation came to light: Many of them were really having thyroid problems.

In a basic thyroid test, a physician will usually have the laboratory perform a "Thyroid Stimulating Hormone" test, or "TSH" test. However, the TSH test only looks at the overall function of the thyroid itself. Therefore, many thyroid problems go undiagnosed because TSH levels can be normal while other problems exist.[102]

Many of these hormones actually float around in your bloodstream attached to a protein, which means they aren't available for use by your body.

Instead, the hormones that are available for us to use are actually floating around in our bloodstream loose rather than attached to a protein. So, it is important to test for these free-floating hormones as well.

Therefore, to get a more accurate reading of how well your thyroid is operating, make sure your doctor is also checking the "free-floating" levels in your blood. Ask your physician about checking both your T4s, which is also called your "Total T4," or "Total Thyroxines," and your Free T3s, or your "Free Thyroxine," levels. These tests will give you a more accurate reading of these levels in your blood.[103]

Heart conditions can also cause you to have reduced brain activity. If someone is suffering from a heart condition, then the blood flowing to that person's brain might be restricted. If that is the case with you, then you will not be getting the proper nutrients and oxygen that your brain needs to function properly.

Therefore, if you have not had a physical within the last year—one that includes full fasting blood work—you need to make an appointment and make sure your overall system is working properly.

Remember: Your brain is a physical organ, just like your heart and lungs. It needs a proper balance of hormones in your body, blood flow, and nutrients to work properly.

# Positive Thoughts, Friends, and Pets

If you think of your emotions or your moods in terms of chemicals, then it is much easier for you to grasp what you will need to do to maintain good brain health. And isn't that what you want? Don't you want to be more productive? Don't you want to be in a good mood? Don't you want to maintain your short-term memory for as long as you can? Don't you want to be happier?

I will assume the answer to these questions is yes. If not, go get a six pack of beer, a dozen donuts, and throw this book at a loved one to begin your own inevitable decline into misery.

First, remember what you think is directly related to what chemicals are being released into your brain. When we think distressing thoughts, we release more adrenaline and cortisol into our system, which makes our muscles tense, our heart rate soar, our glucose levels spike, and our blood pressure rise.

Positive thoughts have the exact opposite effect on our body.

For instance, the chemicals released in our brain when we laugh are very powerful. According to Professor Lee Burk of the University of California at Irvine, "If we took what we know about the medical benefits of laughter and bottled it up, it would require FDA approval. These chemicals can even lower blood pressure and enhance our immune system."

Laughter has been shown to lower blood pressure and enhance our immune system by increasing our number of T-cells and flooding the body with endorphins.[104]

Children laugh hundreds of times a day. Unfortunately, we adults laugh maybe a dozen times throughout the day, at best.

This is one reason I subscribe to satellite radio. I have programmed my presets with several comedy stations. They make me laugh and it makes me feel good. It is a natural high.

I will also download books I want to read and comedy acts I want to hear into my phone so I can listen to them when I am traveling.

When Abraham Lincoln was anxiously waiting for his re-election results in 1864, he read through a book of jokes, laughing and smiling to himself. Many people thought he just didn't care about the results. However, in reality, he was medicating himself. His own intuition told him that laughter calmed him and made him feel better. Neurologically speaking, he was his own best doctor.

Caring for others, like the people do in Roseto, Pennsylvania, releases a wealth of positive eustress chemicals into our body, which is great for our overall health. Actually, caring for others and interacting with positive people is every bit as important as eating a good diet. This is not fuzzy, feel-good stuff. It is neuroscience.

In one study following World War II, researchers discovered that the people who cared for others after the war suffered much less depression and anxiety than those who kept to themselves and did not offer aid to their peers. The old saying, "The more you give, the more you get back," is neurologically true.[105]

In his book, *Love and Survival,* Dr. Dean Ornish, Professor of Medicine at University of California, San Francisco, found those who have close and loving relationships have lower instances of depression, anxiety, suicide, heart disease, infections, hypertension, and cancer.

Yes, altruism is a powerful medicine.

In another study, researchers discovered that whenever military personnel relocated to a new assignment, many transfers developed symptoms of depression. However, if these individuals quickly developed a new social network, friends, a church affiliation, or social groups, recovery came much more quickly.[106]

In a study conducted at Stanford University, women suffering from breast cancer who attended support group meetings every week lived twice as long as those who did not.[107]

To support these studies, brain scans reveal that positive thoughts enhance the ability of our brain to function. Positive thoughts cool the brain's emotional centers, while negative thoughts increase activity in those areas of the brain often associated with depression. Negative thoughts also reduce the ability of our emotional system to function properly, which makes us more vulnerable to fits of anger and unable to control our impulses.[108]

Pets can also help generate a great deal of positive eustress for you. At one time, we had four cats and two dogs. Yes, the animals at one point outnumbered the people.

My cats sit in my office most of the day. They come to see me, just to make sure everything is going all right. They like to look into my camera when I am doing a Zoominar, which most people seem to enjoy. They like to lay on my paperwork, my lap, on the back of my chair, and in front of my window, just to make sure no marauders attack the house. So far, they have done an excellent job.

When I lay down, one of the cats likes to lay on my chest. They are ready to help if there is a problem.

My cats are great for giving me the eustress chemicals my body needs. They relax me.

When Michael was attending graduate school at Roosevelt University in Chicago, he found a cat café to go to and pet the cats. They relaxed and comforted him as he battled the mountain of work he was given working on his master's degree. He says it made him feel much better, which is important if you want to do well in graduate school. (Remember: He graduated with a 3.91 GPA in the middle of COVID.)

Dogs are great too. Some will lie beside you and keep you company, which is great. However, dogs are great for getting your exercise, like playing in the back yard or going on walks. (Trying to take my cat for a walk often ends up with me dragging the cat around the neighborhood by his neck, which will probably get me a visit from PETA one day.)

So, any way you go with pets, they can do a lot in boosting your brain and body's health.

Therefore, the people with whom you associate, the books you read, the work you do and how much satisfaction you derive from whatever you are doing directly relates to the amount of either flooding or Flow you will experience.

## Hobbies

We all need to have hobbies we enjoy that will take our minds off our everyday rat race and fill our bodies with as many eustress chemicals as possible.

One of my hobbies is photography. I love the creative process and the challenge of producing a picture that not only I enjoy but others will as well.

When my sons were in various activities at school, such as in sports, plays, and so on, I would often take hundreds of pictures of all the students participating and post them on Photobucket for all the kids and their parents to download. These photos were a big hit and I felt good at what I was creating. In fact, if I had not gotten any good shots of a particular student, the parent would ask me if I could focus on their kid at the next event so they could have some great shots. I was always happy to do it.

By the way, yes, it really does take a lot of energy to photograph a football game or a track meet. It was great exercise.

I still take pictures of everything. To date, I have over 10,000 edited photographs of my family, mostly of my kids. It gives me a wonderful Flow of eustress chemicals when I do it.

My neighbors like to bird watch. They bring back pictures of eagles, cranes, and other birds that are amazing.

Many people I know love to read. It transports them to not only a different place, but also to another time.

Bowling is another great hobby, as is gardening.

It doesn't matter what hobby you choose. We all need an escape. Hobbies that allow us to escape into the world of Flow are very good for us.

Engaging in your hobby is the same as taking a very healthy eustress drug.

# Meditation

Thanks to brain scans, meditation has taken on a whole new appreciation in the scientific community.

In one study, the brains of Buddhist monks were scanned before and after meditation. Scientists discovered that while the anxiety and anger areas of the brain calmed down during and after meditating, the frontal lobes, or our logical center, actually increased in activity. While many parts of our brains will calm down during meditation, our logical brain, or our prefrontal cortex, will increase its level of activity. That is why meditation makes us much "sharper" mentally.[109]

In another study, the brains of people who either pray or meditate regularly were scanned. The researchers discovered these people calmed their distress and enhanced their brain function through prayer or meditation. These scans revealed that prayer or meditation increased the activity in these people's frontal lobes while having a calming effect on the anger and anxiety centers of the brain. Researchers have also discovered that people who pray and read Holy Scriptures regularly are 40% less likely to suffer from hypertension.[110]

It is important to note, whether you pray or meditate, the benefits are the same from a neurological standpoint. One person's prayer is another's meditation.

In another study at UCLA, the hippocampus—which, again, is our short-term memory transmitter—and the frontal lobes were actually **larger** in people who meditated regularly, which means they had better short-term memory and better focus.[111]

Actually, meditating for only 20 minutes a day for five days has been shown to significantly reduce the distress-related cortisol levels in our bodies.[112]

Meditation has also been shown to reduce depression, improve planning ability, and protect the brain from the cognitive decline typically associated with aging. Meditation has also been shown to help people lose weight, lower blood pressure, control heart arrythmias, reduce muscle tension, and even tighten aging skin.[113]

Meditation can retrain our brains so we do not automatically respond emotionally to stressful situations, just as it does with the Navy Seal recruits. Yes, the logical brain can rewire our emotional and fight-or-flight responses.

Therefore, meditation is a crucial activity in preparing your body to handle and dispel the flooding of adrenaline and cortisol from distress. Today, there are many great meditation recordings, apps and guides to help you.

## Diet

Have you ever heard the expression, you are what you eat? Nothing could be more true.

Anyone who has ever seen Morgan Spurlock's Oscar-nominated documentary, *Supersize Me,* understands the drastic effect a poor diet can have on our health.

In Mr. Spurlock's film, he ate McDonald's food three times a day every day for 30 days. However, before he began this 30-day trek, he had a complete physical. The final verdict was that he was in above-average physical condition before he began this project.

His doctors advised him against eating McDonald's food in this way. Spurlock's doctors predicted that he would gain weight, maybe he would not feel as good, and his cholesterol and triglycerides would rise, but that would be the extent of any real health risks he would encounter.

> **I mean McDonald's is still food . . .**
> **isn't it?**
> **NO . . . IT ISN'T!**

At day 22, Spurlock went into liver failure. He had eaten so much fat and sugar he had clogged his liver and it was shutting down. Spurlock's doctors told him that if he did not end this diet, he would inflict irreparable harm on his body at a minimum, or he might need a liver transplant or might even die.

Spurlock also experienced heart palpitations.

Now, most people can probably understand that Spurlock would gain weight, but liver failure? Heart palpitations? Those are life-threatening conditions.

Actually, after eating McDonald's food every day for every meal for 30 days, Spurlock gained **24 pounds**. That is almost one pound per day. He also consumed **30 pounds of sugar** and **12 pounds of fat** in this 30-day period.

In total, Spurlock developed the following health conditions:

- Heart Palpitations
- Liver Failure
- Depression
- Lethargy
- Headaches
- Mood Swings
- Sexual Dysfunction

Liver failure and heart palpitations are one thing—but becoming sexually dysfunctional? How can your diet affect your mental health and your ability to have sex?

Well, your diet is critical in maintaining good brain health and blood flow. Therefore, we need to think of food as "fuel."

Unfortunately, we are a country addicted to fast food, which is horrible for our brain and overall health:

- In 1970, Americans spent about $6 billion on fast food. By 2021, this spending rose to over $300 billion.[114]
- Every month, approximately nine out of ten American children visit a McDonald's restaurant.[115]
- 37% of U.S. adults consume fast food every day.[116]
- One-third of American children eat fast food on a daily basis.[117]
- One in three babies born in 2000 will likely develop diabetes in their lifetime.[118]
- Eating fast food can cause high levels of insulin, which has been linked to rising incidences of Type 2 diabetes. More than 600,000 new cases of diabetes are diagnosed each year.[119]

For years, western diets and American fast food have invaded China. In 2012, China's Ministry of Health estimated that as many as 300 million Chinese people were obese in a population of 1.2 billion.[120]

However, on December 25, 2020, Nectar Gan of CNN reported that over **half** of all Chinese adults are now overweight. With a population of over 1.2 billion people, there are more obese people in China than live in the entire United States.[121]

Every so often, I think about how we could use the fast food industry to help us with our national defense. As everyone knows, whenever a country goes to war, shots are fired and people get killed. I have also learned that whenever you shoot and kill someone, their friends and family get really mad at you. More than likely, you have just made an enemy for life.

However, I have a modest proposal for the United States. Rather than going to war against an enemy, we should kill them with kindness in an Edgar Allan Poe sort of way. I would propose that we take a few billion dollars or so and build several thousand fast food restaurants throughout the various countries we don't like. We would then open the doors to all its citizens and give them all the fast food they want! The truth is that the entire world loves American fast food. When McDonald's opened a store in Kuwait shortly after the end of the Gulf War, the line of cars waiting to eat there was seven miles long—and these Kuwaitis would pay top dollar to eat this poison. If we just gave away this food to anyone who wants it, in six months, most of the people would be too fat and sick to carry a gun. We would make a lot of friends and undermine the entire country's health simultaneously.

It's just a thought.

Actually, that is happening in the United States right now. Depending on which survey you read, at best, 27% of

Americans ages 17 to 24 years old aren't fit for service in the armed forces, even if they wanted to join, due to them being overweight. When you consider the other health issues these young Americans are suffering from such as asthma or joint problems—issues often related to obesity—as many as 71% aren't fit for service.[122]

Yes, our national addiction to unhealthy food is killing us. Only in America would someone think of opening up a fast food joint and selling a family its meal all thrown into a bucket—which is the same way we feed goats, by the way. Yes, we Americans are very willing to go to Kentucky Fried Chicken and just order a bucket of food for the whole family. Sometimes, we order a couple of buckets.

"Yes, I'd like to order dinner for a family of four and just throw it all into a bucket. That would be great. We'll eat it just like that."

Just in case these fast food facts did not discourage you from eating there, you should probably also know that many of their fountain soda machines contain fecal matter. Of course, that should not be a big concern for you since fecal matter might also be in in the hamburger you are eating, depending on what report you read.[123]

As you can see, I am not much fun to go to lunch with at a fast food joint since I like to point out these little fun facts while you eat.

Still, fast food and other types of restaurants play a vital role in our lives. However, you need to know what you are eating so you can make the best choices you can when perusing a menu. The following website can give you very useful information in making these choices: http://www.fastfood-nutrition.org/

Since our brain burns about 25% of everything we eat, the food we use to fuel our bodies is crucial for our mental health, but it is even more important for our children's developing brains. If children do not receive the nutrition they need, severe mental impairments could result, such as attention deficit disorder, or ADD.

Unfortunately, we have created a society that lives on fast food that contains more saturated fats and simple carbohydrates than vitamins, minerals, and lean proteins.

Therefore, we all need to discover which fruits and vegetables we like and plan them into our diets. If you do not like vegetables, then one solution might be to get a juicer. You can mix in many vegetables and fruits into a juicer. This is a very pleasant way of getting your daily vitamins and minerals.

We do not eat right because chocolate tastes better to most people than carrots and broccoli. This is also why it is easier to get an appointment with God than to get our children to eat their vegetables.

However, getting a good juicer can be a great way to supplement your diet. You can add many vitamins, minerals, and antioxidants to your diet by simply mixing up a pitcher of freshly pureed juice and also adding in such vegetables as carrots, broccoli, cauliflower and so on. You can then store the juice in the refrigerator and drink it the next day. (You want to put your fresh juice into an air-tight container to keep it fresh.)

Many juicers on the market are very good for this purpose. A good juicer will pulverize these vegetables into something you cannot even taste in your juice.

If you are looking for a powerful juicer and one that will not leave any significant leftover pulp, then you should look at a mega-powerful blender like the Vitamix. One of its claims to fame is that it purees food so thoroughly that the Vitamix will actually chop up cell phones. The Vitamix blender is so powerful that it was featured on the History Channel's *Modern Marvel* series.

Although such products can be pricey, it is better to get something that works for you than one that will just sit on the shelf and collect dust.

And no, most bottled fruit juices do not count. They are loaded with sugar, which is bad for you. If you do rely on these, read the labels and get the one with the lowest sugar levels you can find.

## Fats, Carbohydrates, & Proteins

The macronutrients our body needs to function come in three forms:

- Fats, which contain nine calories per gram
- Carbohydrates, which contain four calories per gram
- Proteins, which contain four calories per gram

(We will discuss the vitamins and minerals our body needs, which are called "micronutrients," later.)

## Fats

In recent years, we have been inundated with information on how bad fat is for our body. However, there is a difference between saturated and unsaturated fats.

Saturated fats are what we want to avoid. Saturated fats will give us many health problems, which include making us overweight and damaging our brains.

However, our body needs unsaturated fats. Unsaturated fats have been shown to lower bad cholesterol and raise our good cholesterol. They have also been shown to give us better moods, better memory, and help us to better process our thoughts.

Unfortunately, your body does not produce unsaturated fats, even though our nervous system desperately needs them.

As a result, we must consume them. Otherwise, our brain, and therefore our body, will suffer greatly.[124]

Also, 60% of the solid weight of our brain is fat, most of which comprises our myelin sheath. Our myelin sheath, which is the protective covering that wraps around our nerve endings, keeps the neurons in our brains working properly. When we lose our myelin sheath, our brain will not work correctly. Not only will it become more difficult for us to maintain our focus and concentrate, but there is a great risk of developing many types of mental disorders.[125]

Actually, most of us have seen the horrendous consequences of contracting such diseases as multiple sclerosis and amyotrophic lateral sclerosis, or ALS, which destroy our myelin sheath. That is how critical our myelin sheath is to our health.

In one study, researchers put rats on high saturated-fat diets. Within ten days, the rats developed short term memory loss and lost their desire to exercise. A high level of saturated fats changes our body chemistry to where we become stupid and lazy.[126]

Diets high in saturated fats and sugar, or simple carbohydrates, can also cause you to ignore your feelings of being full for up to three days by overloading your opioid receptors. That is why saturated fats and sugar are addictive.[127]

One way I keep it straight as to which are good and which are bad fats is to think:

> **Saturated fats are saturated with fat.**
> **Unsaturated fats are not saturated with fat.**

**That** makes an impression on me, so I remember. You will want to keep this straight as you read the nutritional guides on the packaging of the food you buy.

For most people, fats should be limited to about 25 grams per day. Controlling our fat intake is actually a lot easier than it was just a few years ago since so many products on the market today are low fat. However, buyers have to be aware:

> **As many products lower their level of fats, they increase the carbohydrates to boost taste.**

## Carbohydrates

Carbohydrates basically come from sugar and starch. However, as soon as a simple starch hits the liver, it turns into a sugar, which raises blood sugar levels. That is why you want to eat more complex carbohydrates, like sweet potatoes, than simple carbohydrates, like white potatoes. Since complex carbohydrates have a more complex molecular structure, they take longer for the body to break them down. Therefore, they do not spike our sugar levels as quickly as simple carbohydrates do, so they give us a much more even burn and help us to maintain a more even blood glucose level for a longer period of time.

When our blood sugar drops, we can lose our self-control, feel anxious and become irritable. That is because our bodies and our brains run on glucose. It is usually at this point that many of us grab a candy bar, chips, or a soda, which will spike our blood sugar levels and put us on our daily glucose roller coaster. When our glucose levels are high, we can feel stressed out and experience high levels of anxiety.

That is why we need to eat three meals a day and eat small healthy complex carbohydrate snacks between meals throughout the day to keep our blood sugar levels in check. This will give us much better control over our glucose levels and therefore our behavior.

Eating snacks like blueberries, strawberries, almonds, and walnuts that have a low glycemic index will help keep your sugar levels from spiking on you. The Glycemic Index website is a great resource that will provide you with the glycemic index of many foods. (See www.glycemicindex.com.)

Eating foods with saturated fats also boosts our glucose levels, while eating lean protein helps to slow down and control the burn of glucose in your body.

Carbohydrates often pose a big threat to many of us because they hide in so many of our food sources. Therefore, reading labels to know what you are actually eating is critical.

Reading the nutritional guides on the sides of food packing is important for knowing what you are eating. However, to determine the carbohydrates you are getting, you need to also look at the fiber content. According to the American Diabetes Association, if a food serving has over five grams of fiber, you can subtract half of the value of the fiber from the total carbohydrates listed.

For example, if a slice of bread has 20 carbohydrates, but it also has 10 grams of fiber, then you would subtract 5 grams from the total carbohydrates. This slice of bread would contain 15 grams of carbs. (10 grams of fiber ÷ 2 = 5 grams of fiber subtracted from 20 grams of carbohydrates in the bread = 15 grams of net carbohydrates.)

Your daily intake of carbohydrates is based upon your body weight and daily calorie needs. To determine the carbohydrates your body needs to function properly, it might be a good idea to seek the advice of a dietician who can calculate this for you.

Also, many sources are available on the internet to determine your proper daily carbohydrate intake. One reliable internet site is www.lifeclinic.com.

There are many excellent "carb cruncher" products on the market, including bagels, breads, muffins, and so on. There are also many excellent sugar-free products on the market.

Stevia is an excellent natural sweetener that as of this writing has not been found to have any negative side effects when used in moderation. Stevia is actually 1,000 times sweeter than sugar. When you first try stevia, use a small amount, not just because of its strength, but because some people may be allergic to it.

Actually, Stevia has been found to also have anti-inflammatory properties and it can help to lower blood pressure.[128]

Personally, I love the Sweet Leaf Sweet Drops. They come in all kinds of great flavors and I can easily add them to my water. I order these directly from Amazon.

There are also many sugar-free and low-carbohydrate jellies and toppings on the market. Bryers also makes very good low-carb ice cream and other frozen products. Sugar-free jello also makes a great evening snack to satisfy that sweet tooth.

There are also several excellent variations of "milk" products on the market you can try. If soy is not your thing, then try almond, rice, or coconut milk. I like the Kroger brand CarbMaster 2% milk. Michael likes rice milk. There are alternatives for everyone.

(Technically, these other products are not really milk. Almonds, rice, and coconuts are not mammals and do not have nipples, so they cannot produce milk. Instead, these are really juices, but marketing people think soy milk sounds better than soy juice.)

Almonds, walnuts, blueberries, raspberries, blackberries, and strawberries are also very good snack choices, rather than grabbing that candy bar every day. You just have to remember to keep them handy. When a Snickers bar is within reach, that is what many of us will grab.

You also need to decide which vegetables you like, then stock up. Steaming vegetables is easier today than ever. Just put your vegetables into a microwavable bowl or plate, put a little bit of margarine or butter on them, which should be low fat and low carb, cover them with a damp paper towel, then set the microwave for four to five minutes. This will usually steam them nicely for you.

It is also worth your time to read the labels of the butter and margarine you are buying. Remember: You want unsaturated fats and complex carbohydrates.

For me, I like to eat raw broccoli and cauliflower with a vegetable dip or salsa. Yes, Michael tells me that neither the dip or salsa are good for me, but they are easy to grab, filling, the vegetables are good for me, and I WILL EAT THEM! The bottom line is that I like them. Again, you've got to find what you like, keep it handy, and treat yourself!

If you are looking to cut down on simple carbs, which often sneak into our diets, do your research by reading about the Diabetic Lifestyle Diet. The internet is loaded with reputable sites that discuss proper eating habits.

Since one out of three Americans is expected to have diabetes in the near future, a good way to prevent the disease is to eat like you are preventing this condition from ever happening to you. There are excellent health-food stores across the country that carry many low-carb products. It is well worth the time to check them out and see what products you like and fit your taste.

To see all that is out there for you, it is also a very good idea to get a pad of paper, a pen, and take a **couple of hours** and walk through your favorite grocery store to read the labels and see what you are eating and what might be a good fit for you. You will be surprised to see how many good products are out on the market that make better choices than what you are currently eating. Take your list of good things with you when you go to the grocery so you will know what is there and what to get.

> **REMEMBER: If you are not prepared and have something good nearby to eat, you will most likely grab some tasty poison.**

## PREPARE, PREPARE, PREPARE!

These websites are excellent sources of nutritional information:

- American Diabetes Association at www.diabetes.org
- The Glycemic Index at www.glycemicindex.com
- The Diabetes Network at www.diabetesnet.com

Knowing what fuel you are putting into your body is critical for total brain health. Planning ahead will make this a much easier battle to fight.

## Proteins

Low levels of serotonin have been linked to depression and mood disorders. It is essential to eat enough protein in balanced amounts with unsaturated fats and complex carbohydrates to maintain a proper balance of eustress chemicals in your body. Not enough protein will leave you with a brain that cannot function properly.[129]

Therefore, get enough lean protein into your diet. Proteins are the building blocks of healthy cells throughout your body. Some of the richest sources of protein are lean fish, lean chicken breasts, cheese, beans, pork, eggs, nuts, and many of the vegetables we eat.

Just so you will not get caught off guard, you should stock up on your protein meats for the week. If you broil chicken, pork, or fish at the beginning of the week, fix an additional amount and put it into a zip lock storage bag or a protective container, like Tupperware. That way, it is ready when you want it. This makes meals and snacking easy, healthy, and tasty.

To enhance dopamine levels, it is best to have protein snacks, such as meat, nuts, eggs, or cheese, and to avoid simple carbohydrates, such as bread, pasta, cakes, and candy.

Protein bars and drinks are excellent for people on the go. However, you always want to read the contents of the bar or drink for carbohydrates, fat, calories, and so on. Not all protein supplements are made the same. I like the Atkins products.

I also like to eat unprocessed whole meat, vegetable burgers or veggie dogs for breakfast. I will either broil my own and have them ready to go, or I will sometimes go to a whole foods deli, like at my local grocery store. Actually, I buy so much high-protein food that one person working there asked me if I was a bodybuilder. (I was wearing a winter coat at the time.) I told her I wasn't. She told me that the only customers who buy food like this are fitness freaks and body builders. I just smiled and said, "Well, maybe more people **should** be eating this way."

Another great snack to always carry with you are Quest Protein Bars. They come in an assortment of great flavors and range from about 180 to 200 calories each. They also contain about 20 grams of carbohydrates per bar with about 18 grams of fiber.

You can read more about them at www.questproteinbar.com.

## Fiber

Fiber, also known as roughage or bulk, includes those parts of plant foods that your body cannot absorb. Unlike other food components, such as fats, proteins, or carbohydrates, which your body breaks down and absorbs, fiber is not digested by your body. Instead, it passes relatively intact through your stomach, small intestine, colon, and out of your body.

Fiber is probably best known for its ability to prevent or relieve constipation. However, foods containing fiber can provide other health benefits, such as helping to maintain a healthy weight and lowering your risk of diabetes and heart disease.

Finding foods you like that contain fiber is easy. Foods we should include in our diets to get our daily fiber requirements are fruits, vegetables, and whole grains. We all need to get enough fiber into our diets, so you will need to look and see what foods you like that contain fiber and add them to your daily meals and snacks.

Fiber is commonly classified as soluble, because it will dissolve in water, or insoluble, which means it does not dissolve in water.

- **Soluble fiber.** This fiber dissolves in water to form a gel-like material. It can help lower blood cholesterol and glucose levels. Soluble fiber is found in oats, peas, beans, apples, citrus fruits, carrots, and barley.

- **Insoluble fiber.** This fiber promotes the movement of material through your digestive system and increases stool bulk, so it can be of benefit to those who struggle with constipation or irregular bowel movements. Whole-wheat flour, wheat bran, nuts, beans, and vegetables, such as cauliflower, green beans, and potatoes, are good sources of insoluble fiber.

Most plant-based foods, such as oatmeal and beans, contain both soluble and insoluble fiber. However, each type varies in different plant foods. To receive the greatest health benefit, eat a wide variety of high-fiber foods.

Refined or processed foods, such as canned fruits and vegetables, pulp-free juices, white breads and pastas, and non-whole-grain cereals, are all low in fiber. The grain-refining process removes the outer coat, or the "bran," from the grain, which lowers its fiber content.

Similarly, removing the skin from fruits and vegetables **decreases** their fiber content. SO, EAT THE SKIN!

Eating a high-fiber diet has many benefits, which include:

- **Normalizing bowel movements.** Dietary fiber increases the weight and size of your stool and softens it. A bulky stool is easier to pass, decreasing your chance of constipation. If you have loose, watery stools, fiber may also help to solidify the stool because it absorbs water and adds bulk to your stool.

- **Helping maintain bowel health.** A high-fiber diet can lower your risk of developing hemorrhoids and small pouches in your colon, which is diverticular disease.

- **Lowering cholesterol levels.** Soluble fiber found in beans, oats, flaxseed, and oat bran may help lower total blood cholesterol levels by lowering low-density lipoprotein (LDL), or "bad," cholesterol levels. Studies also have shown that fiber may have other heart-health benefits, such as reducing blood pressure and inflammation.

- **Helping control blood sugar levels.** In people with diabetes, fiber, particularly soluble fiber, can slow the absorption of sugar and help improve blood-sugar levels. A healthy diet that includes insoluble fiber may also reduce the risk of developing Type 2 diabetes.
- **Aiding in achieving healthy weight.** High-fiber foods generally require more chewing time, which gives your body time to register when you're no longer hungry, so you're less likely to overeat. Also, a high-fiber diet makes a meal feel larger and it stays in your system longer, so you stay full for a greater amount of time. And high-fiber diets also are less energy dense, which means they have fewer calories for the same volume of food.

## How much fiber do you need?

The Institute of Medicine, which provides science-based advice on matters of medicine and health, gives these daily recommendations for adults:

|  | Age 50 or younger | Age 51 or older |
|---|---|---|
| Men | 38 grams | 30 grams |
| Women | 25 grams | 21 grams |

## Fiber supplements and fortified foods

Eating whole foods is generally better than taking fiber supplements. Fiber supplements, such as Metamucil, Citrucel, and FiberCon, don't provide the variety of fibers, vitamins, minerals, and other beneficial nutrients that foods do. However, they are better than not getting any fiber into your diet.

I can also attest to the great value of getting enough fiber into your diet not just from my brain scans, but from my colonoscopies. In case you were interested, I am very proud of my colon, as is my gastroenterologist. It is as clean as a whistle. (I tried to get some photos for this book from my last procedure, but I don't think my doctor's office thought I was serious when I asked for the pics.)

This is not just a fun fact to share with you, but I learned all about a condition called "leaky gut" from Dr. Charles Parker at the Amen Clinic. Yes, sometimes our diet is so bad, which includes a lack of soluble and insoluble fiber, that our small intestines actually start to "leak" fecal matter into our bloodstream. Now, considering that about 25% of what goes into your bloodstream goes to your brain, this can be really bad for your brain's health. This is especially a problem whenever any type of autism spectrum disorder is involved, and leaky gut is often a problem for those with autism spectrum disorder.[130]

## Organic and Free-Range Meats

According to the documentary *Food, Inc.* by Robert Kenner, our food supply has changed more in the last 50 years than it has in the previous 10,000, and not for the better.

For instance, many of our meat sources today, which include our chicken, pork, cattle, and other types of livestock, are often raised on Concentrated Animal Feeding Operations, or CAFOs. This is a factory or industrial system for raising these animals, which causes all kinds of serious problems.

This all started back in the 1950s with McDonald's. The food was fast, cheap, and tasted great. The fast food industry then demanded that beef producers provide them with even cheaper beef in huge quantities. Today, McDonald's is the largest purchaser of beef in America, so the producers must comply with its demands. That means the beautiful pastures filled with happy cows eating grass are almost gone. The large producers must instead raise their cattle on an industrial scale if they want to survive.

In 1970, the top five producers of beef controlled only 25% of the market. Today, the top four beef producers control 80% of the market. So, factory farming is now the norm.

The same situation also applies to the pork industry. Today, 60% of our pork is controlled by four corporations.

> **So, even if you don't eat fast food, you are still likely eating CAFO-produced meat.**

The first problem with CAFOs is that they pack the animals in together so tightly that they can hardly move, which means these animals are forced to stand and live in their own feces and urine. Due to these horrendously unsanitary conditions, these animals are much more susceptible to disease and illness, as are we when we eat their meat. So, to combat this disease and illness, these animals are injected with high doses of antibiotics, which we also will consume. Such conditions will not only result in us eating "high risk" food that can harm our brains and our bodies, but it can also result in bacteria that can kill us, like E. coli and salmonella.[131]

However, this industrial scale of food production has made beef cheap. Unfortunately, the average American now eats over 200 pounds of beef every year.

Today, 99% of all the farmed animals in the U.S. live in factory farms.[132]

When the debate surrounding world hunger comes up, it is hard to ignore this intensive increase in animal agriculture, which has resulted in about one-third of all the world's cropland being solely dedicated to growing animal feed. This is a tremendously inefficient use of our resources.[133]

In 1950, it took about 70 days to raise a chicken for market. However, by the year 2008, chicken producers had cut that down to only 48 days, and these chickens are now twice as big as the ones we raised in the 1950s. These chickens are now engineered to grow so big that many of them cannot walk over two or three steps without falling down. However, the consumers want bigger breasts, so they get them.

These chickens are then packed into darkened chicken coops, so they never see the light of day. Every day, workers must walk through these darkened chicken coops and pick up the ones who died the previous day. This is not exactly what you see in their television commercials.

Antibiotics are put into their feed to keep them from getting sick in these horrendous conditions. Many workers who come into contact with this feed have developed a resistance to antibiotics.

The fact that factory farms increase the risk of antibiotic resistance should be a great concern to everyone. According to the World Health Organization, around 80% of the world's antibiotics are given to farmed animals. Misusing antibiotics in this way causes these bacteria to mutate and then become resistant to antibiotics. This is a major health threat for all of us. Today, antibiotic resistance kills 700,000 people each year. By 2025, that number is expected to skyrocket to ten million people. By 2050, it is expected that more people will actually die from antibiotic resistance than cancer. Yes, in the near future, small cuts can kill. That is why antibiotic resistant bacteria has been named as one of the biggest threats to global health. Of course, you won't have to worry too much about your brain health at that point because you'll be dead.[134]

A key ingredient in these factory farms is corn. Today, corn is king. It is in almost everything you buy at the grocery store, which includes everything from fruit juice to ketchup to Motrin. The reason corn is used so much is not just because of its versatility as a starch. Instead, the large food manufacturers are so rich and powerful that they have forced Congress to subsidize corn to where it can now be produced and sold below its actual cost. So, these large multinational food producers get these subsidies from the government and produce as much corn as they can. As a result, 30% of America's farmland is dedicated to growing corn.

So, corn is fed to the animals in these CAFOs. It is not only really cheap, but it will fatten up the cows, chickens, and even farm raised fish. Actually, 90% of all the cows and pigs sent to market are raised on a corn diet.

In order to maximize the growth of these animals, growth hormones are also often used. In the end, factory-farmed meat has a high-fat content and lacks vital nutrients.

Since the government greatly subsidizes the production of corn, and not raw fruits and vegetables, the greatest predictor of obesity is one's income. Yes, cheap food, like pretzels, chips, factory-farm-raised meats and so on are what many people living near or below the poverty level can afford to buy. Also, most of these foods entice our biological taste buds since they are filled with saturated fats, sugars, and salt. We can all buy hundreds of more calories of food in the snack food aisle than in the vegetable section.

The additional problem for the cows, and for us, is that they cannot digest corn. Cows were designed to eat grass. So, the cows get sick from eating all of this corn, and since they are also standing ankle-deep in urine and feces all day, they are given even more antibiotics.

We then eat these antibiotics and growth hormones, which is not good.

There is also the special case of E. coli. Since these cows are raised on corn, which they cannot digest, a mutated form of E. coli called "E.coli O157:H7" has developed. Coupled with the fact that these cows are standing ankle deep in manure all day long, if one gets E. coli, many other cows will get it as well. By the time they get to the slaughter house, their carcasses are covered in manure. So, if the slaughter house is processing 400 cows an hour, how could you ever keep the manure from getting into the meat? You can't.

This problem is then made worse when you consider that one hamburger could contain pieces of meat from a thousand different cows.

You should now better understand my earlier comment about having fecal matter in your hamburger.

> **Interestingly, if these CAFOs were banned, and the cows were fed grass for one week instead of corn, the E. coli would die off.**

But then, that would cut into these large corporations' profits, so that will not happen anytime soon.

A report by the National Association of Local Boards of Health states that "CAFO manure contains a variety of potential contaminants. It can contain plant nutrients such as nitrogen and phosphorus, pathogens such as E. coli, growth hormones, antibiotics, chemicals used as additives to the manure or to clean equipment, animal blood or the copper sulfate used in footbaths for the cows."[135]

But what if you are good about eating a brain- and body-healthy diet and eat mostly vegetables? Why are we always hearing of spinach being recalled because of E. coli contamination? Spinach does not eat corn or stand all day in its friends' manure.

Well, it is pretty simple. As our friends the cows stand in their feces all day, it also rains. The raw feces then flow into the river. When the feces-laden river water gets to the farmers living downstream, they spray this manure-water all over their vegetables. Later, we buy it, eat it, and get sick. What is even worse is that sometimes it kills the most vulnerable among us: our children.

In case it was not obvious to you, manure water is bad for humans—and most everything else, except for pathogens.

But don't we have the Food and Drug Administration, or the FDA? Don't we have regulations and government oversight? Well, not really.

Unfortunately, several experts believe that the FDA is one of the most "dysfunctional" federal agencies in existence. On August 20, 2012, *Forbes Magazine* published an article entitled, "FDA SpyGate -- the Government's Most Dysfunctional Agency" by John Entine.

In this article, *Forbes Magazine* claimed that the FDA's entire culture is dysfunctional. The article claimed that the FDA is corrupt because it has been bought and paid for by large corporations, like these multinational food corporations, and by the pharmaceutical companies. (We will talk about the pharmaceutical companies here shortly.) The article also claimed that the FDA's culture punishes those employees who blow the whistle on the FDA's corruption.[136]

For example, in 1972, the FDA conducted about 50,000 food inspections. However, about 40 years later in 2006, just as factory farming methods were becoming the norm, the FDA conducted only 9,164 inspections. Personally, I take little comfort with enforcement like that going on.[137]

Today, the FDA is pretty much toothless, and that is how many of these multinational food corporations want it.

And if you have not heard enough good news, CAFOs are the perfect place for creating dangerous pathogens that can spread from animals to humans. Scientists have warned that factory farming could create future pandemics that may be more deadly than COVID-19. Get ready. The world-wide pandemics did not end with COVID. The next one, and we **will** have another one, may likely come from the United States.[138]

Also, we have been using many different types of pesticides, which includes insecticides, herbicides, rodenticides, and fungicides for many years. The goal of pesticides is to destroy pests without negatively affecting humans and the environment. I actually found an old advertisement that read, "DDT is GOOD for me!"

Even though pesticides have gotten better over time, none are perfect at providing pest control without having side effects for humans. Unfortunately, the safety limits for pesticides are often established using incomplete data or studies funded by the food manufacturing corporations or the pesticide producers themselves. Although more research is needed, it is believed that ingesting pesticides can contribute to the buildup of heavy metals in the body. Experts also believe that many of the other long-term health effects of pesticides can be difficult to detect. Still, experts believe that exposure to pesticides may be linked to a higher risk of Parkinson's disease, Alzheimer's disease, and several types of cancer. Some studies show that pesticide exposure could be linked to a higher chance of being diagnosed with cancer, ADHD, and autism spectrum disorder.[139]

Unfortunately, pesticide residues are in up to 70% of produce sold in the US, according to the latest annual analysis by the U.S. Department of Agriculture.[140]

Clearly, organic and free range raised meats are best.

So, what does this mean to you? Avoid pesticides as much as possible. ORGANIC, ORGANIC, ORGANIC! Remember, about 25% of everything you put into your mouth is going right to your brain—and that includes pesticides.

## Plant Based Diet—Just A Thought

Of course, one obvious solution for you to think about is adopting a more plant-based diet, which my whole family is now doing. We are always looking for good, healthy alternatives, such as plant-based hotdogs, hamburgers, and so on. We are finding some great products on the market that we love and they are safe for us to eat.

Just something to consider.

## Antioxidants

Getting enough antioxidants into your system is also important. Antioxidants can reduce the free radicals and toxins that circulate throughout our bodies, thus allowing a better flow of blood and nutrients to the brain, which will greatly reduce our risk of cognitive impairment. Antioxidants are commonly found in various fruits and vegetables. This is yet another reason to eat your fruits and vegetables!

If you do not eat approximately five servings of fruits and vegetables each day, and if juicers are not your thing, then another option is to take an antioxidant nutritional supplement. There are several products on the market today you can use to meet your daily nutritional requirements. Typically, these nutritional supplements come in powder or liquid form, which you can then mix with either water or juice. Therefore, these powders and liquids are simple and easy to use.

What you should look for in these products is a high oxygen radical absorption capacity, or ORAC. ORAC is a measurement used to indicate the total antioxidant power of foods and other chemical substances. The higher the ORAC measurement, the more antioxidant power the food source has to neutralize free radicals. Therefore, determining a food's ORAC level is one way to measure how many free radicals a specific food can absorb. The more free-radicals a food can absorb, the higher its ORAC score. Antioxidants eliminate the free radicals from the human body.

Using the antioxidant powder is easy. You just mix it with water, milk, or juice (one that is low in sugar), and drink it. You simply do this once a day and you are done.

However, nothing is as good as just eating your fruits and vegetables.

Eliminating free radicals from the body is critical for many reasons.

First, free radicals can break down and destroy the body's healthy cells, which can cause cancer.[141]

Also, since the brain burns about 25% of everything in our blood stream, good brain health means keeping the free radicals out of our system. Too many free radicals in our system can lead to brain impairment.[142]

Our bodies produce free radicals every time a cell converts oxygen into energy. In normal amounts, free radicals will not harm us. Actually, they can help the body eliminate harmful toxins.

However, when we have too many free radicals in our system, they can cause the cells in our bodies to deteriorate. This is called "oxidative stress," which causes cell death and tissue damage. This effect on the body is similar to rusting metals when exposed to moisture in the air. Antioxidants act as the body's "rust inhibitors," thus the name antioxidant.[143]

When this happens in the brain, we have just damaged our brain and our ability to function.

This is why blueberries have been referred to by neuroscientists as "brain berries." Blueberries are particularly high in antioxidants, so they are extremely effective in ridding the brain of excess free radicals. Therefore, blueberries can help us to develop new motor skills, protect us from strokes, improve our blood sugar levels, lose body fat, and to lower bad cholesterol.

However, only eat organic berries. Berries can also retain large amounts of pesticides.

I love to eat berries in low fat milk with Stevia or Truvia sprinkled on top. It is a great dessert. I see berries as a "free food." I can eat as many as I want! You will always find fresh berries in our refrigerator.

## Omega-3 Fatty Acids

The human brain also needs omega-3 fatty acids to operate properly. That is why omega-3 fatty acids are classified as "essential fatty acids," or "EFAs." They are *ESSENTIAL* to the human body—which includes your brain.

However, even though omega-3 fatty acids are essential to human health, the human body cannot manufacture them. So, we need to consume them, which means we must all either eat more foods like fish two or three times a week or take an omega-3 supplement.

Our bodies have adapted themselves to rely on omega-3 fatty acids for a logical reason: It was much easier for Fred Flintstone to catch and eat fish a few times a week rather than catching and eating a couple of lions. Clearly, Fred preferred to battle a bunch of fish than a bear or a lion, as I am sure you would too.

There are two major types of omega-3 fatty acids we can include in our diets:

- One type is alpha-linolenic acid (or ALA), which is found in some vegetable oils, such as soybean, canola, flaxseed, and walnuts. ALA is also found in some green vegetables, such as brussel sprouts, kale, spinach, and salad greens. Since our bodies will partially convert ALA to EPA and DHA, many vegetarians will consume foods rich in ALA so their bodies will get the necessary amount of EPA and DHA.

- The other types, EPA and DHA, are found in fatty fish, like salmon.

The DHA portion of omega-3s help to build up and maintain the "insulation," or the myelin sheath, around the neurons in your brain so they can work more efficiently. Again, our myelin sheath is critical to our brain's health because it allows our brain cells to work **ten to 100 times more efficiently**, much like the insulation surrounding the copper wires in our homes.[144]

DHA is also essential for maintaining brain and retinal function. DHA accounts for up to 97% of the omega-3 fats in the brain and up to 93% of the omega-3 fats in the retina. Since our eyes are really an extension of our brain, DHA is needed in the retina, the light-sensitive part of the eye.[145]

I have been diabetic for about 15 years. Every year, I visit my optometrist and get both of my eyes mapped to see exactly how my retinas are doing. I am proud to say that my retinas are looking great, just like my colon. I might have diabetes, but I also have my omega-3s.

The EPA portion of omega-3s is another essential fatty acid. Although only trace amounts of EPA are found in the brain, EPA helps to improve brain function by maintaining a healthy blood flow, influencing our hormones and boosting our immune system.

## Dietary Sources for Omega-3 fatty acids

Fish, plant, and nut oils are the primary dietary source of omega-3 fatty acids. EPA and DHA are found in cold-water fish such as salmon, mackerel, halibut, sardines, tuna, and herring.

The American Heart Association recommends eating fish (particularly fatty fish such as mackerel, lake trout, herring, sardines, albacore tuna, and salmon) at least two times a week.

However, due to the high levels of mercury found in our fish supply, we need to be very careful about the fish we eat. We should also make sure the omega-3 fatty acid dietary supplements we take are certified as being mercury-free by a reputable third-party lab.

The famous speaker and author Tony Robbins adopted a presumably healthy diet that included fish. After a while, he was rushed to the hospital. He had developed mercury poisoning. He was losing his memory, it had burned a hole in his esophagus, and he lost one-third of his blood.

So, to see what types of fish are best for you to eat, just go to www.seafoodwatch.com.

It is also a good idea to check the mineral levels in your blood every so often.

Personally, I would never even think of eating farm-raised fish. I think the conditions in which these fish are raised are revolting. Unfortunately, 70% of all of the fish on the market today comes from artificial fish farms.[146]

The problem with these fish farms is often the same as we saw with the chicken and cow CAFOs. These fish are usually packed together by the thousands. The fish then develop parasites and lice. So, the fish are given antibiotics, pesticides, and disinfectants, which are toxic, to combat these issues, which we then eat.[147]

About an ounce, or one handful, of walnuts have about 2.5 grams of omega-3s, according to the American Dietetic Association. That is equal to about 3.5 ounces of salmon.[148]

For me, I like to buy the pouches of wild-caught salmon from the grocery store. I will then put a pouch of salmon on top of my dark greens salad. I will also sprinkle a handful of walnuts on top. To help keep my blood sugar more stable, I will sprinkle cinnamon all over it as well. Sometimes, if I feel motivated, I will hard boil eggs and put those on my salad as well. It all tastes great and it is good for me. I try to eat what I call my "big salads" a few times a week.

Michael is also a big salad fan, but he does not put any salad dressing on his. I do because choking on my lunch is no way to live.

For added vitamins, Michael also loves to put beets on his salads.

The bottom line is that making your salad is a very personal thing for you. Look around and get many things you like that are healthy, including your omega-3 fatty acids.

The American Dietetic Association also says that eating whole foods rather than taking supplements is much better for you. When you eat whole foods, about 90% of the omega-3s are absorbed into your body. However, with many supplements, only about 50% to 80% of the nutrients are actually absorbed into your body. That is why it is important to check the solubility of the vitamin supplements you are taking to make sure as much as possible is absorbed into your circulatory system before they reach your bladder.[149]

To get your proper amount of omega-3s and remain safe from mercury contamination, two servings of fish a week at three to four ounces per serving is recommended. That portion size is well below the FDA's safe limit of 12 ounces per week to avoid mercury contamination.[150]

If you are a vegetarian, then you need to look for sources of omega-3 fatty acids from something other than fish. Flaxseed oil is a natural and rich source of ALA omega-3 fatty acid. ALA is also found in flaxseeds, canola oil, soybeans, soybean oil, pumpkin seeds, pumpkin seed oil, walnuts, and walnut oil.[151]

Dr. Amen of the Amen Clinics recommends that adults take approximately 2,000 mg of omega-3 fatty acids which contain a combination of EPA and DHA. If an adult is battling some specific condition which omega-3s could help, then 2,000 mg to 4,000 mg might be appropriate.[152]

## Vitamins and Minerals

The micronutrients our body needs, or vitamins and minerals, are critical for our health. Unfortunately, most of us do not get the vitamins and minerals we need as part of our diets in order for our bodies to function properly, much less our brains.

I was once presenting my "Brain Health" seminar to a group of physicians at a hospital just south of Columbus, Ohio. When I got to the section on vitamins and minerals, specifically on the subject of taking a daily multivitamin and mineral complex packet, I was virtually attacked by these doctors.

"You are just telling people to waste money on these packets and all anyone ever gets from these vitamins is expensive urine. All people need to do is eat a balanced diet and they will get everything they need!" I was told.

"So, do you tell your patients **not** to take a daily multivitamin or a mineral complex packet? Do you tell your patients that taking these packets will only result in expensive urine?" I asked.

"Of course," they responded. "All they need to do is eat a balanced diet. They will be fine."

"OK," I responded. "So, which vitamins will they urinate out?"

They looked at each other, then one blurted out, "All of them."

"Oh, no," I responded. "Only certain vitamins are water soluble and only water-soluble vitamins will be urinated out. The rest are fat soluble. So, if you take too much of a fat-soluble vitamin, it will be stored in the person's fat cells. The excess vitamin can then become toxic. So, if you are telling your patients that all of these vitamins are water soluble, then they could be overdosing on these vitamins thinking they won't do them any harm."

I then leaned forward and asked them point blank, "So, which vitamins are water soluble and which are fat soluble?"

There was then a very uncomfortable silence. They didn't know . . . but that did not keep them from voicing an opinion on the matter. (Yes, the facts only get in the way of a good opinion.)

I told them that **only** vitamins B and C are **water soluble**. All other vitamins are **fat soluble**. This means if we ingest too much vitamin C or any of the B vitamins, we will simply urinate out the excess—as long as we don't actually **try** to overdose on them.

Surprisingly, some of these physicians also did not know the difference between a vitamin and a mineral.

If you are going to take care of your body, especially if you are going to take multivitamins and a complex mineral packet, know what they do and what you are putting into your body.

So, what is the difference between vitamins and minerals?

First, vitamins and minerals are different, although we often group them all together.

Vitamins, like vitamin C, help your body work properly. Minerals, on the other hand, are actually absorbed into and become part of your body, like calcium.

Also, vitamins are organic substances made by plants or animals, whereas minerals are inorganic elements that come from the earth, such as from the soil and the water absorbed by plants. Animals and humans then absorb these minerals from the plants they eat. However, both vitamins and minerals are nutrients that your body needs to grow and develop normally.

The body cannot produce minerals. Minerals, such as calcium, must be absorbed through our food. Other minerals like chromium, copper, iodine, iron, magnesium, selenium, and zinc are called "trace minerals" because you need small amounts of them each day.

There are many different vitamins and minerals our body needs to function properly. However, since over 90% of all Americans do not eat the way they should to meet their daily nutritional needs, we need to seriously think about taking a daily multivitamin and mineral packet.[153]

Also, most people over the age of 50 have trouble absorbing vitamin B12 into their system. That is just a natural part of aging. That is one reason many manufacturers make vitamin and mineral packets specifically for people over the age of 50.

Having even a slight deficiency of vitamin B12 can lead to anemia, fatigue, and depression, since it plays a key role in helping the central nervous system function. If someone is deprived of vitamin B12 for a long period of time, serious damage to the brain and central nervous system can be the result. Vitamin B12 is also important for helping us to maintain our metabolism and to form red blood cells.

Again, there is little chance you could take too much vitamin B12 because it is water soluble. If you take more than you need, you will just urinate it out.

Unfortunately, our food supply today does not contain the vitamins and minerals our bodies need, which makes it even more important to take a quality vitamin and mineral packet every day.

First, as most people know, today's food manufacturers strip away many of the vitamins and minerals from our food due to the processing methods they use.

Next, there is a serious concern over the depletion of our soil. In fact, crops grown decades ago were much richer in vitamins and minerals than what we are eating today.

On April 27, 2011, *Scientific American* published the article, "Dirt Poor: Have Fruits and Vegetables Become Less Nutritious?" This article clearly stated that the fruits and vegetables grown decades ago were much richer in vitamins and minerals than what we are eating today, and the main problem causing this lack of nutrition trend is soil depletion. Modern farming methods have stripped away many of the nutrients we need from the soil. With every passing generation, our faster growing, pest-resistant vegetables have less and less nutritional value when compared to the ones we were eating years ago.

The article relied heavily on the research conducted by Dr. Donald Davis and his team of researchers from the University of Texas at Austin's Department of Chemistry and Biochemistry. Dr. Davis' team studied the nutritional data from the U.S. Department of Agriculture from both 1950 and 1999 covering 43 different fruits and vegetables. The team found there were "reliable declines" in the amount of protein, calcium, phosphorus, iron, vitamin B2, and vitamin C across this time frame. There have also more than likely been declines in other nutrients, according to Dr. Davis, such as magnesium, zinc, and vitamins B6 and E.

Davis and his colleagues found this remarkable decline in the nutritional content of our food supply was due to the changes we have made to our farming practices to grow our food faster, bigger, and more pest resistant rather than focusing on its nutritional value. Specifically, Dr. Davis said:

> "Efforts to breed new varieties of crops that provide greater yield, pest resistance and climate adaptability have allowed crops to grow bigger and more rapidly," reported Davis, "but their ability to manufacture or uptake nutrients has not kept pace with their rapid growth."

For example, 100 years ago a farmer could get 20 bushels of corn per acre. Today, that same farmer can easily get 200 bushels of corn from that same acre.[154]

Dr. Davis and his team are not alone in making such findings. The article went on to cite other studies that supported Dr. Davis' conclusions. In a similar study conducted by the Kushi Institute, the team of researchers analyzed the nutritional data of our food from 1975 to 1997. They found that average calcium levels in 12 fresh vegetables dropped 27%, the iron levels dropped 37%, the vitamin A levels dropped 21%, and the vitamin C levels dropped 30% across this time period.

The article also cited a study conducted on the food grown in Great Britain from 1930 to 1980. This research team found that in the 20 vegetables they studied, the average calcium content had declined 19%, the iron content had declined 22%, and the potassium content had declined 14%.

Another study cited by *Scientific American* concluded that you would have to eat *eight oranges today* to derive the same amount of vitamin A as our grandparents would have gotten from **one** grown years ago.[155]

There are many different minerals that the human body needs to function properly.

Minerals basically serve three roles in the human body:

1. They provide structure in forming bones and teeth.
2. They help maintain normal heart rhythm, muscle contractility, neural conductivity, and acid-base balance.
3. They help regulate cellular metabolism by becoming part of enzymes and hormones that modulate cellular activity.

Therefore, consuming enough minerals in our diet is crucial for our health.

## Choosing Multivitamin and Mineral Packets

Again, the vast majority of Americans do not eat the required five servings of fruits and vegetables every day. And even if they do, they are still not getting the level of nutrition they need.

In the June 19, 2002 issue of *The Journal of the American Medical Association* (JAMA), two scientists from the Harvard Medical School recommended that all adults take daily vitamin supplements. These new guidelines were groundbreaking since they reversed the AMA's 20-year anti-vitamin policy.

The AMA's new recommendations were:

1. Most people do not consume enough vitamins through their diets alone.
2. After reviewing nearly 40 years of clinical research, the AMA definitively concluded that vitamin supplementation plays an important role in preventing common chronic diseases such as cancer, stroke, heart disease, and osteoporosis.

Specifically, the AMA said:

"... insufficient vitamin intake is apparently a cause of chronic diseases. Recent evidence has shown that suboptimal levels of vitamins, even well above those causing deficiency syndromes, are risk factors for chronic diseases such as cardiovascular disease, cancer, and osteoporosis. A large proportion of the population is at increased risk for this reason."[156]

However, choosing a good multivitamin and mineral packet is very important. You should always question what you are putting into your body.

Many physicians frown on over-the-counter supplements because they are not approved by the Food and Drug Administration, or the FDA.

However, the FDA doesn't test anything. The pharmaceutical companies have their drugs tested and evaluated, and then they submit the results to the FDA for approval. Remember, the FDA is also the same organization that brought you such wonderful drugs as Vioxx, Fen-Phen, Seldane, and a host of other drugs that have killed or seriously harmed hundreds of thousands of people. Every year the FDA recalls drugs it has approved and placed on the prescription market.

Again, just as it is with the large multinational food corporations, the FDA is "dysfunctional" and "corrupt" when it comes to pharmaceutical companies, according to *Forbes Magazine.*

Also, the pharmaceutical lobby in Washington, D.C. is one of the most powerful groups influencing our public policy, as is the fast food lobby. (It also concerns me that some physicians and psychiatrists get "kickbacks" for prescribing certain medications to their patients.)

Therefore, whenever you choose a supplement, make sure that the manufacturer has put its product through a vigorous testing and verification program. Just because the supplement was not submitted to the FDA for approval does not mean it was not tested and verified the same as a prescription strength medication.

First, if you buy just any multivitamin or mineral packet, how do you know there are any vitamins or minerals in it? Because it says so on the package? You don't.

Also, since every vitamin and mineral are absorbed by the body at different rates, how do you know the manufacturer has tested its product and verified that the supplements you are buying will be absorbed into your body?

And how do you know there are not any contaminants in the over-the-counter supplements you are buying?

Well, you first want to make sure that any supplements you take are produced under Good Manufacturing Practices, or GMP. GMPs are guidelines that provide a system of processes, procedures, and documentation to ensure that a product really does have the ingredients, strength, composition, quality, and purity that it says it contains.

So, when choosing your supplements, make sure that the manufacturer follows the GMP standards.

United States Pharmacopeia, or USP, is the official pharmacopeia in the U.S. USP and the National Formulary publish their standards under the name USP-NF. USP also sets standards for food ingredients and dietary supplements.

Make sure that the supplements you are taking not only meet but exceed these USP standards.

An excellent website to join that rates the various supplements on the market is www.consumerlab.com.

Of course, this might be more research than most people want to do, so I recommend to my clients to consider products from such reputable companies as Shaklee, AdvoCare, and GNC. These organizations are adamant about maintaining high standards in the types of products they sell.

Michael and I get our brain supplements from the Amen Clinics website, BrainMD.com. We take two of the Brain & Body Power Max multi-vitamin and mineral packets every day. These are the best and most powerful multi-vitamin and mineral packets I have found. I pop these two packets throughout the day, I eat a healthy balanced diet of the foods I like, and it works. It has everything a supplement packet can give you every day.

Our latest brain scans will back me up on that, as you have seen.

## Water

It is vital to your brain's health that you drink several glasses of water every day. Since our brains are 80% water, it is extremely important to keep our brains hydrated.

> **If you are human, you need to drink half of your weight in ounces of water every day.**[157]

Otherwise, your brain will simply "dry out," and it will not work properly.

In one study, professional body builders had their brains scanned when they were training for a competition. When they are training, bodybuilders keep themselves well hydrated. While they were hydrated, their brains looked very healthy from their nuclear brain scans.

However, in the week when these bodybuilders are actually competing, they dehydrate themselves to appear more muscular. These same bodybuilders then had their brains scanned again. This time, their brains looked like they were drug addicts. The difference between their hydrated and dehydrated brains was remarkable after only one week of not properly hydrating themselves.

The moral: **hydrate, hydrate, hydrate.**

Dehydration is also the problem we run into when we drink too much caffeine or alcohol:

> **They dry out the brain, which hinders its ability to function.**

Far too often, I will hear that drinking coffee, soda, tea or some other drinks high in caffeine or salt will also count as drinking water. That is simply not true.

Caffeine also blocks "adenosine," a chemical that tells us when it is time to go to sleep.[158] As a result, we can have trouble not only getting to sleep but staying asleep throughout the night.

While other types of drinks are liquid, they are not as good as water.

Since caffeine dries out the brain, for every two steps you move forward in drinking water, you take one step back when you drink anything containing caffeine.

And drinking too much salt not only dries out the body, but it suppresses our immune system and raises our insulin resistance, which boosts our sugar levels and makes us more susceptible to diabetes.[159]

The answer: **water, water, water!**

I actually keep several large tumblers of water at my desk at all times. When I finish one, I grab the other one sitting there.

I also have a great collection of traveling water containers that are insulated to keep everything cold. Drinking enough water is a big key to brain health!

Other drinks should be viewed as a "treat."

## Get Enough Sleep

You also need to make sure you are getting enough sleep.

In 1900, Americans got about nine hours of sleep each night. In 2008, we averaged about six hours of sleep. Studies show that humans who get less than six hours of sleep experience a significant reduction in blood flow to their brain, which harms its ability to clean out toxins.[160]

We sleep in 90 minutes cycles. At the end of this sleep cycle, we go into REM sleep, which stands for rapid eye movement. You can tell if you have entered REM sleep because that is when we dream.[161]

When we go into REM sleep, we are actually cleaning out the excess cortisol that has built up throughout the stressful day. When we do not get enough REM sleep, we not only feel grouchy because there is still too much cortisol remaining in our brain, but allowing this added cortisol to remain behind can put additional distress on our brain. Therefore, getting enough REM sleep is a major factor in repairing and maintaining a healthy brain.

If you do not get enough sleep, your brain will see this as an additional stressor. As a result, even more cortisol will be released into your system, which can work to compound the flooding in your brain and body. Therefore, getting enough sleep is a major factor in combating distress.

When you go into REM sleep, that is also when you transfer information from your short-term to your long-term memory.

So, if you want to be able to accurately recall what happened the previous day, you need to get your sleep.

Getting seven to eight hours of sleep each night will also help get better blood flow to your brain. If you do not get enough sleep at night, you will not have enough blood flow to your frontal lobes the next day for them to work properly, which means you will not have enough oxygen to supply your brain as it tries to function. Good blood flow is critical for our frontal lobes to do their job, and yes, you really will need your frontal lobes the next day.

> **Sleep therefore rejuvenates the brain. Without it, we can actually become psychotic.**

Getting a good night's sleep is essential to becoming and remaining an emotionally intelligent person.[162]

Sleep also restores the energy resources to your brain, which is vital for it to function properly. I discussed how important it is to refill your brain's gas tanks every night in my first book, *Solve Employee Problems Before They Start*, but it is worth mentioning it again here.

Your brain operates much like a car's engine. To operate effectively, your brain, and specifically your frontal lobes, works best when it has a full tank of resources, or neurotransmitters. These neurotransmitters act like the gasoline that keeps your car running. If you run out of gas, your frontal lobes will slow down and your emotional system can take control. That is when really bad things happen.[163]

When we sleep, we restore these vital resources for our brain to operate efficiently the next day.

The left frontal lobe in particular has a very important job in relation to our emotions and our fight-or-flight response. Our left frontal lobe acts as the brain's neural thermostat for our emotions.

Humans typically experience about 150,000 emotions each year, which is about 27 emotions every waking hour, all of which must be controlled by the frontal lobes. That is one very important reason why you really need to have a full tank of gas, healthy blood flow and a full supply of resources to your frontal lobes every day: to exert control over your ego and emotions.

The left frontal lobe usually does a good job of keeping our emotions in check. Think of it this way: What our emotions and fight-or-flight systems generate, the left frontal lobe regulates.

Unfortunately, it takes tremendous resources to keep our frontal lobes operating properly. However, it takes virtually no effort or resources at all for our emotions and our fight-or-flight systems to surge out of control. They can run on automatic without consuming hardly any resources at all.[164]

Therefore, it is critical that we get enough sleep each night to refill the neurotransmitters in our brain in order to remain in control the next day.

It is also important to understand that we use up many of our neurotransmitters in our brain as the day goes on. Think of your frontal lobes working like a car's transmission. The more you change gears throughout the day, the more resources you will use. Although focusing on the same project for hours at a time will greatly deplete the brain's resources, changing directions and dealing with many different issues throughout the day will deplete the brain's resources even faster.[165]

So, your brain works the same as if you were driving your car through the downtown area or on the expressway. If you are driving through the city, you would shift gears all the time, using up more gas. But if you are going 70 mph on the highway, you won't burn nearly as much gas because you are not shifting your gears all the time.

We make many kinds of decisions throughout the day. We control our basic urges to speak out and retaliate against others. We keep our mouths shut when we hear or see things that offend us. Unfortunately, by the end of the day, we have used up a lot of these vital resources. That is why it is so much easier to stick to our diets in the morning than at night. This is also why it never ceases to amaze me that humans often save our most critical and highly emotional conversations until the end of the day when our tanks are almost empty. And then we are actually surprised when these conversations don't go well.

We would never think of starting our car and traveling across town on an empty tank. (Well, most of us wouldn't. ) Cars simply do not run when there isn't any gas in the tank. The same is true of our frontal lobes.

Dealing with highly emotional situations also helps to explain why fights can get so personal and out of hand late at night. People are tired and have used up most of their brain's resources throughout the day, and the oxygen supply to the frontal lobes is greatly reduced. People get emotionally hijacked by their amygdalae and end up feeling really sorry and embarrassed in the morning, and maybe trying to explain everything to the police—or a judge. Think of it this way: We all want to make sure our tanks are full when we engage in highly emotional situations. Sleep is what refills our tanks.

Again, it takes a tremendous amount of resources to keep your logical brain working properly. However, our emotional system doesn't require any resources at all. So, when our brain runs low on gas, our emotional system will easily take over, which is not going to be good for you.

I think of this neurological fact every time I have to coach someone, give someone a written warning, or even fire them. In business, we often think it is best to deliver a written warning or terminate someone at the end of the day. However, that is a really good way to get a stapler thrown at your head. The person facing discipline is tired and running low on gas. And now, at the end of the day, you want to deliver a highly emotional message to this person? And you want this person to process this highly emotional information accurately and keep their emotions under control?

Good luck with that.

I prefer to handle highly emotional or difficult conversations at the beginning of the day when we are all fresh. If it is a written warning, I will often send the person home for the rest of the day to think about the problem. It is better to focus on the issue at hand in the comfort of your own home than at work.

This is just another reason you should never assume that just because you said something it means that the other person processed that information accurately. Since most people you meet are sleep deprived, that means:

- Their brain is not getting enough blood flow and oxygen.
- Their brain is retaining too much cortisol.
- That person is most likely operating on less than a full tank of gas.

Yes, we should all just assume the other person is indeed brain impaired.

That is just another reason why I always use my EPR skills in any conflict situation. EPR, which stands for Empathic Listening, Parroting, and Rewards, ensures that I really did hear and understand what the other person told me, and they agreed that I understood it correctly. When I listen to what someone is telling me from their perspective, which is Empathic Listening, and I then repeat it all back to their satisfaction, which is Parroting, I know we are all on the same page.

This is also a CYA thing. Later, someone cannot lie and say that we had a misunderstanding. I repeated it back to you, and you agreed that I understood, so there was no misunderstanding there.

Without gaining a common understanding between the two parties, there will never be a proper resolution to a conflict.

One of the best indicators as to whether you have some sort of mental impairment is how well you sleep. People typically think if someone is depressed that they sleep less or that they have trouble falling asleep. While that might be true for some people, one of the tell-tale signs that someone is suffering from depression is that they will fall asleep rather normally, but they will wake up early in the morning, like at 2:00, 3:00, or 4:00 am. That is why if you go to the emergency room with a case of clinical depression, someone will ask you if you are waking up in the wee hours of the morning. If so, the chances you are suffering from depression just skyrocketed.

Yes, sleep is a big deal to combat the distress in your life and build a healthier brain.

So, how can you get better sleep?

First, get your fasting blood work and your complete physical done. If there is a chemical imbalance or some other physical issue going on, you need to address it. That alone has solved the problem for many people I coach.

The other stress management factors I mention in this book can also help, such as exercise, massage, meditation, hanging around good people, and so on. All of these factors can increase the eustress chemicals in your body, which can help get you into a better sleep pattern.

There are also L-tryptophan supplements that you can take to prepare you for better sleep. Taking these an hour before you are ready for bed can be useful for some people.

Melatonin is also a natural supplement that can help make you sleepy before bedtime. Taking a small three milligram tablet can do wonders in getting you to sleep at night.

If you are still having trouble sleeping, seriously consider going to see a sleep specialist. You need your sleep.

## Exercise and Sex

We all need to treat our exercise like it is just as important as taking our medications. Just as with many of the other outlets for distress we have discussed, engaging in exercise can increase our blood flow, get more oxygen throughout our body, dispel adrenaline and cortisol, and generate eustress chemicals, such as serotonin, dopamine, endorphins, and so on.

Additionally, exercise generates the "brain-derived neurotrophic factor" protein, or BDNF. BDNF is needed for growing new neurons in the brain. BDNF works like "Miracle Grow" in the brain for neurons.[166]

Again, our brain grows about 100,000 new neurons every month, mostly in our hippocampus, which is our short term memory transmitter. However, if these new neurons are not nourished with BDNF, they will die within four weeks.[167]

Physical exercise can be very healing for your emotional system since it can physically alter the chemical compounds in your brain, which constitutes your mood.[168] People in good physical condition are usually in high spirits after an exercise session, sometimes to the point of elation or joy. People who engage in long, continuous, gentle exercise enjoy the most effective stress therapy known to man. Therefore, exercise directly affects how well you can handle the distress in your life.[169]

Specifically, exercise releases endorphins and L-tryptophan, which is a precursor to serotonin that gives us a sense of well-being and balances our moods. It can help us recover from depression. Our deep limbic system, or our emotional system, has many endorphin receptors, which make it prime to benefit from increased activity.[170]

Exercise also releases glutathione, which is a powerful antioxidant. Therefore, exercise can help with the healing process.[171]

Research also tells us that exercise moves lymph through our lymphatic system. Lymph is a clear-to-white fluid made of white blood cells, especially lymphocytes, which are the cells that attack bacteria in the blood. Exercise makes the muscles contract and pushes lymph through the lymph vessels. This can reduce swelling and help us to recover from illnesses faster.[172]

L-tryptophan is a very small amino acid when compared to the other amino acids of the body. When we are not exercising, our various amino acids, including L-tryptophan, line up to get through the blood brain barrier and enter the brain. However, because the L-tryptophan amino acid is so small, it has a very difficult time getting past the other much larger amino acids.[173]

It is a lot like the Munchkins from *The Wizard of Oz* trying to push the Ohio State Buckeyes out of the way to get into a crowded bar. The Munchkins stand little chance of succeeding.

However, when we exercise, the Buckeyes are called to go play in the game and the Munchkins are left behind. (No, you really shouldn't put a Munchkin in at left tackle.) So, the Munchkins can just dolly on in through the door unopposed.

That happens when we exercise. I have had several clients tell me they have exercised their way off their psychotropic medications—under the supervision of their physician, of course.

Exercise also helps with wound healing, preventing and lessening the effects of dementia, calming worries and anxiety, easing the effects of ADD, giving us better control over our behavior, helping us sleep better, and maintaining a better hormone balance, to mention a few.[174]

Regular exercise can also lower your distress chemicals while increasing your eustress chemicals, as well as making you tired, which helps you get a better night's sleep.[175]

Studies show that 20 to 30 minutes of daily exercise at 60% to 80% maximum capacity will reap the highest positive effects for your daily moods. However, physical activity that is less intense but is longer in duration will also work. The exercise that is the least effective in altering our moods is short, high-intensity workouts.[176]

> **Exercise increases the blood flow to your brain.**
>
> **This also acts to remove the waste products that collect in our brains, such as cortisol.**

Also, since exercise increases the amount of blood that runs through our brain, the brain becomes better nourished so it can function properly. Think of it like a radiator flush for your brain. Just as your body does not operate well if you do not have good blood flow, the same is true for your brain. Good blood flow in the brain will also "reset" your emotional system to a healthier level, which improves our mood.[177]

As is also the case when we engage in our hobbies, socialize with positive people, eat right, and so on, when we exercise, we turn off those genes designed to harm us and we turn on those genes designed to keep us healthy. That is just another reason why exercise is a miracle drug.

For most healthy adults, the Department of Health and Human Services (DHHS) recommends these guidelines for maintaining our physical health:

- **Aerobic activity.** Most adults need at least 150 minutes a week of moderate aerobic activity, like walking, or 75 minutes a week of vigorous aerobic activity, like a treadmill or a stair stepper. There is nothing wrong with engaging in both moderate and vigorous activity.

  Moderate aerobic exercise includes such activities as brisk walking, swimming, and mowing the lawn. Vigorous aerobic exercise includes such activities as running, using low impact machines at a brisk pace, and aerobic dancing.

  Actually, early man walked about five miles a day, which was great for his physical health. However, thanks to cars, elevators, escalators, and so on, most of us walk much less than that.

- **Strength training.** Most adults need to engage in strength training at least twice a week. While the DHHS does not give us any specific amount of time for each strength training session, work your entire body.

  Strength training can include using free weights, weight machines, resistance bands, push-ups, and even heavy gardening.

To lose weight, you will need to exercise even more. I have clients exercising 60 minutes a day to get back into shape.

However, the most important point to remember is that you need to pick exercises you like and make them part of your lifestyle.

In rebuilding my body and my brain, I like to use my glider for my aerobic exercise. I can watch my television, maybe pop in a DVD, and step away. I like to work at a moderate pace for 30 to 45 minutes, depending on my time constraints.

I also set up a portable basketball court in my backyard. Since I am a towering five foot six inches tall, I have never been a great basketball player. However, in my own backyard court, I can work up a sweat and win NCAA championships for Ohio State all the time.

For years, I had two rescue dogs, Ella and Sophie, who loved to play soccer. I just called them "the girls." So, I got a soccer ball and inflated it about three-quarters of the way. I then went out in the backyard with the girls and we played soccer. Keeping up with the girls was rough; but it was great exercise, they loved it, and it was a lot of fun for me.

Actually, the day we got Ella fixed, I let her out into the back yard. She picked up her soccer ball and took off running. So, Ella, Sophie, and I all played soccer that afternoon. When my wife got home, she looked at me like I was crazy.

"We just got her fixed and you took her out to play soccer?" she asked.

Yeah, I kind of saw her point there.

I also like to fight "Boxing Bob" every so often. Bob, who has no arms or legs and cannot hit back, is set up in the corner of my basement. I put on my Velcro-strapped boxing gloves and beat the heck out of Bob. After 15 to 20 minutes of this, I am spent. It is a great workout and a GREAT way to release the stress of the day.

Also, there is nothing wrong with putting the jersey of a sports team you hate on Bob, or maybe the mask of someone's face you want to pummel. It is better to do it to Bob than to those people in real life—and if it motivates you, hey, game on!

For my strength training, I have a simple barbell set up in my basement. I can do several exercises with a single barbell—and watch TV while I do them.

I have also joined a gym where I have a set routine I follow. It takes me about an hour and 15 minutes to get through it.

To make my workout time at the gym special, I like to listen to music on my iPod—music I have actually downloaded legally from the internet. The only time I allow myself to listen to my iPod is when I work out. For this hour, I am in my own little world where I can listen to my music and sort through various issues in my head. It is a great get away time just for me.

My youngest son, Nicholas, also likes to go to the gym with me to work out. This is a great thing we can do together. We can motivate each other to get to the gym and work out several times a week.

I also have special workout towels I like to take with me to the gym. I take regular hand towels of all colors and iron patches onto them I like. I have towels with Batman, Superman, Underdog, Mighty Mouse, Ohio State, the Cincinnati Bengals, and any other patches I find entertaining. It just makes it fun.

Since gyms are a cornucopia of germs, workout towels are not only important for wiping off your own sweat, but I put them between my head and the disease-laden equipment. I also take my own spray bottle of rubbing alcohol mixed with water. There is no way in the world I will trust the watered down antibacterial foam the gym gives you to use.

If you are going to lift weights or use your hands to grip any bar in your exercise routine, you need to get a pair of padded weight lifting gloves. Since you have several delicate nerve endings in your hands, gripping the bar without protection can damage those nerves. Padded gloves will help protect them.

Since I also have a broken back and a torn rotator cuff, I have special exercises I do to strengthen my upper and lower back and my rotator cuffs.

When you do your resistance training, always remember what you are doing is tearing your muscles apart. Yes, you are ripping them into shreds. When they repair themselves, they will come back bigger and stronger than before.

So, you want to do your repetitions in a nice, slow steady manner. Too many people use momentum to get their weights or machine moving too quickly. This is actually more aerobic training than strength training, so it is not the best way to build muscle. It is also a good way to injure yourself.

Since you actually build the most muscle on the last few repetitions you do, you want to squeeze out repetitions in a slow and controlled manner.

You also do not want to put too much weight on yourself when doing your resistance training. Your goal is to build strength, not bulk. I assume no one reading these materials is looking to enter a bodybuilding contest, but are just interested in building a strong body that will serve them well in the years to come.

Personally, I am not only training my way out of a torn rotator cuff, a broken back, PTSD, and diabetes, but I am training for being 90 years old.

Exercise can:

1. Give you more energy and keep you from feeling lethargic.
2. Increase your metabolism and help keep your appetite in check, which will help keep your weight down.
3. Help to normalize the production of melatonin in your brain, which will enhance your sleep cycle.
4. Allow more of the amino acid serotonin to enter the brain, which enhances your mood.

Yes, you will be happy to know that having sex is part of the doctor's orders. In fact, having sex three times a week is recommended.[178]

Having sex has been shown to lower your risk of heart attack and stroke by 50%. It has also been shown to help with pain relief, improve depression, and boost serotonin levels and memory. Dr. Daniel Amen says if sex was a drug, it would need FDA approval! There is simply no medication on the planet that can do as much for you as good old sex.

If your significant other objects, get a prescription from your physician. You have to follow your doctor's orders, right?

# Massage

Getting a massage can also release many of these same healing chemicals we get from experiencing eustress. That is why we feel so good and small problems simply do not rattle us as much after we have just gotten a massage.

For instance, imagine that you have just gotten a massage. You are relaxed. You feel great. Many of your worries seem far behind you.

You then get into your car and pull out into traffic when another driver cuts you off in traffic and almost hits you in the front end. How do you react? Ordinarily, we probably yell and scream at the other driver. However, since we just had a massage and have a nice balance of eustress chemicals floating through our body, we say, "What the heck. He missed me."

Why can we retain our cool much more easily after getting a massage? Because of the eustress chemicals in our body.

> **Massages change the chemical balance in our system.**

The medical profession recognizes the beneficial effects of massage to where some insurance plans will cover it as a medical expenditure. Also, since many states will tax the cost of getting a massage, get a prescription from your physician. That way, you can give this prescription to your massage therapist and the session will not be taxed.

If you have a back condition, your health insurance plan might cover part of the cost of your massage.

By now, you should have written down three things you can start doing now. So, that means it is time to get started!

# Final Thoughts

Michael and I hope we have put things into an easy to understand format so you will all know . . .

- How your brain works,
- What is good for your brain,
- What is bad for it, and
- How to put together your own personalized brain health program.

We also hope we have made it clear that there are some basic practices that must be included in your own personalized brain health program, such as:

- Eating a good diet,
- Taking vitamin and mineral packets,
- Drinking half your weight in ounces in water every day,
- Exercising,
- Getting good people, thoughts, and meaning into your life,
- Getting your physical and fasting blood work,
- Starting your meditation and/or prayer routine,
- Getting your sleep, and of course . . .
- Getting as many jackasses out of your life as possible.

Those are the basic rules we followed for rewiring our brains. However, as they say, there are many roads to Rome. In other words, your program might not look like Michael's or mine. You need to design your own program filled with things you like for each of these basic rules, not what Michael or I like or what we did. Still, the basic rules of brain and body health remain the same.

In the end, you need to realize that you are responsible for maximizing your mental and physical health as much as possible. No one else can do it for you. You do not want to live like most people do because we as a human race are not heading in the right direction. The personal stakes for you are just too high to ignore.

I hope you all see by now that the power to change and improve lies within you. No one can do it for you. It is up to you to take charge of yourself and improve your own life.

> **There are no superheroes coming to help you and they couldn't help you even if they did come along.**

But then, you don't need them. Again, the power to improve your life lies deep within yourself if you follow the guidelines we put into this book. You must become your own superhero.

Again, Michael and I wrote this book because . . .

> **We wanted to prove to the world we can all rewire our brains, improve our mental conditions, and maybe even cure them.**

So, the power for change lies with you. But with that, I will leave you in the same place we started this book, which is what we should all have moving forward:

**HOPE.**

# WILL YOU SHARE THE LOVE?

## Get this book for a friend, associate, or family member!

If you have found this book valuable and know others who would find it useful, consider buying them a copy as a gift. Special bulk discounts are available if you would like your whole team or organization to benefit from reading this. Just email scott@scottwarrick.com or visit www.scottwarrick.com.

# Would You Like Michael and Scott Warrick to Speak to Your Organization?

## Book Michael and Scott Now!

Michael and Scott Warrick accept a limited number of speaking/coaching/training engagements each year. To learn how you can bring their message to your organization, email scott@scottwarrick.com or visit www.scottwarrick.com.

# Review Inquiry

Hey, it's Scott and Michael here.

We hope you've enjoyed the book, finding it both useful and fun. We have a favor to ask you.

Please write to us at scott@scottwarrick.com and let us know what you thought of the book. Could you relate to Scott's story, or Michael's or both, and have you had these experiences in your own life? Did it help you better understand how your brain works and how to protect it? What did you do to change the way you live? What was the most helpful part of the book? **We would love to hear from you.**

Would you also consider giving it a rating wherever you bought the book? Online book stores are more likely to promote a book when they feel good about its content, and reader reviews are a great barometer for a book's quality.

So please go to the website of wherever you bought the book, search for our names and the book title, and leave a review. If you liked the book and if you thought it deserved an A, please give it five stars. If able, perhaps consider adding a picture of you holding the book. That increases the likelihood your review will be accepted!

Many thanks in advance,

Scott and Michael Warrick

# BIBLIOGRAPHY

"About Brain SPECT Imaging." Amen Clinics.

https://www.amenclinics.com/approach/why-spect/#:~:text=Brain%20SPECT%20(single%20photon%20emission,and%20activity%20in%20the%20brain

Amen, Daniel. "Brain Health Professional Certification Course." Amen University, 2022.

https://www.amenuniversity.com/professional-brain-health-certification

Amen, Daniel. *Change Your Brain, Change Your Body.* New York, NY: Harmony Books, February 16, 2010.

Amen, Daniel. *Change Your Brain, Change Your Life.* New York, NY: Three Rivers Publishing Group, 1998.

Amen, Daniel, *Healing the Hardware of the Soul.* New York, NY: Free Press, 2002.

Amen, Daniel. *High Performance Brains.* MindWorks, 2012.

Amen, Daniel. *Magnificent Mind At Any Age.* New York, NY: Three Rivers Publishing Group, 2008.

Amen, Daniel, et al. "Specific ways brain SPECT imaging enhances clinical psychiatric practice." *Journal of Psychoactive Drugs,* April-June 2012.

"Are Pesticides in Foods Harming Your Health?" *Healthline.*

https://www.healthline.com, medically reviewed on May 26, 2021.

"Behavioral endocrinology." *Wikipedia,* 2022.

https://en.wikipedia.org/wiki/Behavioral_endocrinology

Beurkens, Nicole. "Treating the Gut is Vitally Important for Autism Spectrum Disorders." *Holistic Child Psychology,* drbeurkens.com, April 17, 2018.

https://www.drbeurkens.com/gut-treatment-for-autism-spectrum-disorders/

Bouchez, Colette. "Good Fat, Bad Fat: The Facts About Omega-3: Think all dietary fat is the same? Guess again." *WebMD*, December 12, 2008.

https://www.webmd.com/women/features/omega-3-fatty-acids

Bradberry, Travis and Jean Greaves. *The Emotional Intelligence Quick Book.* New York: Fireside, 2005.

Brondolo, Elizabeth, DiGiuseppe, Raymond, and Tafrate, Raymond Chip. "Exposure-based Treatment for Anger Problems: Focus on the Feeling." *Cognitive and Behavioral Practice,* 1997.

https://www.ccsu.edu/criminology/iscj/files/Exposure_based.pdf

Brooks, Sarah. "10 Shocking fast food facts." *SheKnows, sheknows.com,* July 1, 2013.

https://www.sheknows.com/food-and-recipes/articles/996693/10-shocking-fast-food-facts/

Brockway, Ludo, Brockway, Otto. *Eating Our Way to Extinction.* October 1, 2021.

Camargo, EE. "Brain SPECT in neurology and psychiatry." *Journal of Nuclear Medicine,* April, 2001.

"Can Exercise Make Me High?" *HealthCentral.com,* September 17, 2001. Adapted from "The Fit or Fat Woman" by Covert Bailey and Lea Bishop, published by Houghton Mifflin Company.

Catafau, AM. "Brain SPECT in clinical practice, Part I: Perfusion." *Journal of Nuclear Medicine,* February 2001.

Chai Feldblum and Victoria Lipnic. "EEOC Select Task Force on the Study of Harassment in the Workplace: report of co-chairs Chai R. Feldblum & Victoria A. Lipnic." *EEOC.gov.* Equal Employment Opportunity Commission, 2016.

https://www.eeoc.gov/select-task-force-study-harassment-workplace-report-co-chairs-chai-r-feldblum-victoria-lipnic

"Cingulate Gyrus. " *Physiopedia.*

https://www.physio-pedia.com/Cingulate_Gyrus

Clifton, Jim. "The World's Broken Workplace." *The Chairman's Blog.* Gallup, June 13, 2017.

https://news.gallup.com/opinion/chairman/212045/world-broken-workplace.aspx.

Collin, Graham. "Magnetic Revelations: Functional MRI highlights neurons receiving signals." *Scientific American Magazine*, October 2001.

Costa, DC. "The role of nuclear medicine in neurology and psychiatry." Institute of Nuclear Medicine, University College and Middlesex School of Medicine, London, UK, *Current Opinion Neurol Neurosurgery*, December 5, 1992.

Covington, Maggie. "Omega-3 Fatty Acids." *American Family Physician*. 2004 Jul 1;70(1):133-40
>    https://pubmed.ncbi.nlm.nih.gov/15259529/

"Dietary fiber: Essential for a healthy diet." Mayo Clinic, January 6, 2021.
>    https://www.mayoclinic.org/healthy-lifestyle/nutrition-and-healthy-eating/
>    in-depth/fiber/art-20043983

"Difference Between B-Cells and T-Cells." *Easy Biology Class*.
>    https://www.easybiologyclass.com/difference-between-b-cells-and-t-cells-
>    comparison-table/

Diraddo, Danielle. "15 Surprising Facts and Statistics About The Fast Food Industry." *Toast*, 2021.
>    https://pos.toasttab.com/blog/on-the-line/fast-food-industry-statistics

"Dopamine."
>    https://en.wikipedia.org/wiki/Dopamine.

Domonell, Kristen. "This Is Your Body On Fear." *UW Medicine*, October 25, 2017.
>    https://rightasrain.uwmedicine.org/well/health/your-body-fear-anxiety

Entine, Jon. "FDA SpyGate -- New Revelations Challenge The New York Times Investigation of Agency 'Enemies List,' Raise More Questions About the 'Government's Most Dysfunctional Agency.'" *Forbes*, August 20, 2012.
>    https://www.forbes.com/sites/jonentine/2012/08/20/fda-spygate-new-
>    revelations-challenge-the-new-york-times-investigation-of-agency-enemies-
>    list-raise-more-questions-about-the-governments-most-dysfunctional-agency/

"Exercise, positioning and lymphoedema." *Cancer Research UK*, accessed June 10, 2022.
>    https://www.cancerresearchuk.org/about-cancer/coping/physically/
>    lymphoedema-and-cancer/treating/exercise#:~:text=Positioning%20yourself
>    &text=Make%20sure%20you%20fully%20support,the%20head%20of%20
>    the%20bed

"Fight-or-Flight Reaction." *ChangingMinds.org.*

http://changingminds.org/explanations/brain/fight_flight.htm

Fletcher, Robert and Kathleen Fairfield, MD, DrPH. "Vitamins for Chronic Disease Prevention in Adults." *JAMA,* June 19, 2002.

https://jamanetwork.com/journals/jama/fullarticle/195038#:~:text=We%20reviewed%20the%209%20vitamins,vitamin%20C%2C%20and%20vitamin%20K

French, Paul. "Fat China: how are policymakers tackling rising obesity?" *The Guardian,* February 12, 2015.

https://www.theguardian.com/global-development-professionals-network/2015/feb/12/chinas-body-mass-time-bomb-policymakers-tackling-rising-obesity

Gan, Nectar. "More than half of Chinese adults are now overweight. That's more people than the entire US population." CNN, December 24, 2020.

https://www.cnn.com/2020/12/24/china/china-adult-overweight-intl-hnk/index.html

Gates, Donna, EdD, MSPH, MSN, RN, "Stress and Coping: A Model for the Workplace," *AAOHN Journal, Volume:* 49 issue: *August 1, 2001.*

Gladwell, Malcolm. *Blink.* Little, Brown, and Co., New York, NY, 2005.

Goleman, Daniel. *Emotional Intelligence.* New York, NY: Bantam, 1998.

Goleman, Daniel. *Social Intelligence: The New Science of Human Relationships.* New York, NY, Bantam, 2006.

Grubin, David, *The Secret Life of the Brain: The Child's Brain,* PBS, 2005.

*Haltiwanger, John.* "America Is So Out of Shape and Fat, It's Putting U.S. Army Soldiers in Danger." *Newsweek,* January 11, 2018.

https://www.newsweek.com/america-so-out-shape-and-fat-its-putting-us-army-soldiers-danger-778840

Hamilton, Ryan. *How You Decide: The Science of Human Decision Making.* The Great Courses, Chantilly, VA: The Teaching Company, 2007.

Henson, Priscilla, MD. "Addiction & Substance Abuse in Lawyers: Statistics to Know." American Addiction Centers, March 22, 2022.

https://americanaddictioncenters.org/rehab-guide/workforce/white-collar/lawyers

Holman, Devous, MD. "Functional brain SPECT: the emergence of a powerful clinical method." *Journal of Nuclear Medicine,* October 1992; 33(10):1888-904.

> https://jnm.snmjournals.org/content/33/10/1888

"Innate Immune System." *Wikipedia.*

> https://en.wikipedia.org/wiki/Innate_immune_system

Insel, TR. "Judd Marmor Award Lecture." American Psychiatric Association Annual Meeting, 2005, Atlanta, GA.

Kenner, Robert, *Food, Inc.* Magnolia Home Entertainment, 2009.

Kobayashi, Nobuhisa, Kato, Motoichiro, and Hoeft, Fumiko. "Contribution of neuroimaging in the prediction of outcome in neuropsychiatric disorders and learning disabilities." *Brain nerve,* October 2007.

Krausz, Yodphat, Omer Bonne, Rami Marciano, Susan Yaffe, Bernard Lerer, RolandChisin, "Brain SPECT imaging of neuropsychiatric disorders." *European Journal of Radiology,* 1996.

> https://www.sciencedirect.com/science/article/abs/pii/0720048X95007256

Lakna. "What is the Difference Between Allostasis and Homeostasis?" *PEDIAA. com,* July 26, 2019.

> https://pediaa.com/what-is-the-difference-between-allostasis-and-home ostasis/#:~:text=The%20main%20difference%20between%20allostasis, conditions%20maintained%20by%20living%20systems

LeDoux, Joseph. *The Emotional Brain.* New York: Simon and Schuster, 1996.

LeDoux, Joseph. *Synaptic Self: How Our Brains Become Who We Are.* New York: Penguin Books, 2003.

Levitan, Clarisse. "Why 85% of People Hate their Jobs," *Staff Squared,* December 3, 2019.

> https://staffsquared.com/blog/why-85-of-people-hate-their-jobs/

Lock, S. "Statistics and Facts about the Fast Food Industry." *Statista.com,* 2016.

> https://www.statista.com/topics/863/fast-food/

Makary, Marty. *The Price We Pay: What Broke American Health Care--and How to Fix It.* New York, NY: Bloomsbury Publishing, 2019.

McKay, Hannah. "Mega Farms Called CAFOs Dominate Animal Agriculture Industry." *Sentient Media*, September 29, 2021.

  https://sentientmedia.org/cafo/

Meaney, Michael J. "Nature, Nurture, and the Disunity of Knowledge," *Annals of the New York Academy of Sciences* 935, 2001.

Merrill, Scott. "Legal Field has High Rates of Substance Abuse, Mental Illness." *Concord Monitor*, July 19, 2021.

  https://www.concordmonitor.com/Legal-profession-suffers-with-high-rates-of-substance-misuse-and-mental-illness-41484963

"Military Suicide Rates Are at an All-Time High; Here's How We're Trying to Help." United Service Organizations, June 27, 2022.

  https://www.uso.org/stories/2664-military-suicide-rates-are-at-an-all-time-high-heres-how-were-trying-to-help

Nicholson, Christie. "No Fair! My Serotonin Level Is Low," *Scientific American*, June 9, 2008.

  https://www.scientificamerican.com/podcast/episode/68fc98f1-e48a-251d-8f65277181db9a4e/

Norden, Jeanette. *Understanding The Human Brain*. The Great Courses, The Teaching Company, 2007, Vanderbilt University School of Medicine, Nashville, TN.

O'Connell, RA, Van Heertum, RL, et al. "Single photon emission computed tomography (SPECT) with [123I] IMP in the differential diagnosis of psychiatric disorders." *Journal of Neuropsychiatry and Clinical Neuroscience*, 1989 Spring; 1(2): 145-53. Article Number: UI92330314.

O'Connell, RA, Sireci, SN, Jr., Fastov, et al.: "The role of SPECT brain imaging in assessing psychopathology in the medically ill," *General Hospital Psychiatry*, September 1991, 13(5):305-12. Article Number: UI92077409.

"Oxygen & Deforestation." The Conscious Club, April 30, 2019.

  *https://www.theconsciouschallenge.org/ecologicalfootprintbibleoverview/oxygen-deforestation*

Parker, Charles. *New ADHD Medication Rules: Brain Science & Common Sense*. Virginia Beach, VA: Koehler Studios, 2012.

Powledge, Tabitha. "The Dope on Dopamine's Central Role in the Brain's Motivation and Reward Networks." *Scientific American*, September 15, 2008.

> https://www.scientificamerican.com/article/dopamines-central-role-brains-motivation-reward/#:~:text=The%20Dope%20on%20Dopamine's%20Central%20Role%20in%20the%20Brain's%20Motivation%20and%20Reward%20Networks,-Researchers%20use%20two&text=Researchers%20have%20for%20the%20first,that%20it%20changes%20with%20age

Rawlence, Christopher. *Secrets of the Mind.* NOVA, 2001.

Reinberg, Steven. "Surgical Tools Too Often Left Behind in Patients." *HealthDay Reporter*, WebMD, October 17, 2013.

> https://www.webmd.com/a-to-z-guides/news/20131017/surgical-implements-too-often-left-behind-in-patients-report#:~:text=According%20to%20the%20commission%2C%20there,have%20their%20hospital%20stay%20extended.

"The Role of Dopamine." *The Brain from Top to Bottom.* Mcgill University.

> https://thebrain.mcgill.ca/flash/i/i_03/i_03_m/i_03_m_que/i_03_m_que.html

Sapolsky, Robert. "Stress and Your Body." The Great Courses, Chantilly, VA: The Teaching Company, 2010, Stanford University, Menlo Park, CA.

"Dirt Poor: Have Fruits and Vegetables Become Less Nutritious?" Earth Talk. *The Scientific American*, April 27, 2011.

> https://www.scientificamerican.com/article/soil-depletion-and-nutrition-loss/

Rosling, Claire. "Serotonin: A Molecule of Happiness." University of Bristol, UK.

> www.chm.bris.ac.uk/motm/serotonin/home1.htm

Siegel, Ronald. "The Science of Mindfulness." The Great Courses, Chantilly, VA: The Teaching Company, 2007.

Smith, Andrew F. *Encyclopedia of Junk Food and Fast Food.* Westport, CT: Greenwood Press, 2006.

Song, Huan, MD, Ph.D., Fang Fang, MD, Ph.D., Gunnar Tomasson, MD, Ph.D., et al, "Association of Stress-Related Disorders With Subsequent Autoimmune Disease." *JAMA,* June 19, 2018.

> https://jamanetwork.com/journals/jama/fullarticle/2685155

"Sources of Greenhouse Gas Emissions." Environmental Protection Agency, 2020.
https://www.epa.gov/ghgemissions/sources-greenhouse-gas-emissions#:~:
text=The%20primary%20sources%20of%20greenhouse,share%20of%20
greenhouse%20gas%20emissions

Sparks, Dana. "TUESDAY Q & A: Establishing a daily routine first step for teen
with chronic pain." Mayo Clinic, July 2, 2013.
https://newsnetwork.mayoclinic.org/discussion/tuesday-q-a-establishing-
a-daily-routine-a-good-first-step-for-teen-with-chronic-pain/#:~:text=
Although%20the%20thought%20of%20exercising,take%20the%20edge%20
off%20pain

Spoehr, Thomas and Handy, Bridget. "The Looming National Security Crisis:
Young Americans Unable to Serve in the Military." Heritage Foundation, February
13, 2018.
https://www.heritage.org/defense/report/the-looming-national-security-
crisis-young-americans-unable-serve-the-military

Stoppler, Melissa Conrad. "Endorphins: Natural Pain and Stress Fighters."
*MedicineNet.*
https://www.medicinenet.com/endorphins_natural_pain_and_stress_
fighters/views.htm

Sauter, Steven, et al. "STRESS...At Work." The National Institute for Occupational
Safety and Health, 1999: 99-101.
https://www.cdc.gov/niosh/docs/99-101/default.html

Stojanovich, Ljudmila, and Marisavljevich, Dragomir. "Stress as a trigger of
autoimmune disease." *Autoimmunity Reviews,* November 29, 2007.
https://pubmed.ncbi.nlm.nih.gov/18190880/

"Stress in America 2020: A National Mental Health Crisis." American Psychological
Association, 2020.
https://www.apa.org/news/press/releases/stress/2015/snapshot

Heminway, John. *Stress: Portrait of a Killer.* National Geographic, 2008.

Spurlock, Morgan. *Fast Food and the Supersizing of America.* New York, NY: Penguin
Group (USA) Inc, 2005.

Tang, Wilson. "SPECT vs PET," *Radiopaedia,* June 8, 2021.
https://radiopaedia.org/articles/spect-vs-pet

Taylor, Victoria. "Unhappy in America: Nearly 70% of U.S. employees miserable at work, study finds." *New York Daily News,* January 28, 2015.

> https://www.nydailynews.com/life-style/majority-u-s-workers-not-engaged-job-gallup-poll-article-1.2094990

"US Military Officials Worried: Are Young Americans Too Fat?" *VOA News,* July 25, 2019.

> https://learningenglish.voanews.com/a/us-military-officials-worried-are-young-americans-too-fat-/5002588.html

Vagg, Richard. *The Brain.* The History Channel, 2009.

Vasile, RG. "Single photon emission computed tomography in psychiatry: current perspectives." *Harvard Rev Psychiatry,* 4(1):27-38 1996 May-Jun.

> https://pubmed.ncbi.nlm.nih.gov/9384969/

Walsh, Bryan. "Getting Real About the High Price of Cheap Food." *TIME Magazine,* August 31, 2009.

> http://content.time.com/time/subscriber/article/0,33009,1917726,00.html

"Whitehall Study." *Wikipedia.*

> https://en.wikipedia.org/wiki/Whitehall_Study

Woolston, Chris. "Type 2 Diabetes and Kids: The Growing Epidemic." *Health Day,* May 15, 2022.

> https://consumer.healthday.com/encyclopedia/diabetes-13/misc-diabetes-news-181/type-2-diabetes-and-kids-the-growing-epidemic-644152.html

"Workplace Violence." United States Department of Labor. Occupational Safety and Health Administration.

> https://www.osha.gov/workplace-violence

Zametkin, A J; T.E. Nordahl; M. T E; Gross, M; King, A C; Semple, W E; Rumsey, J; Hamburger S; Cohen R M. "Cerebral glucose metabolism in adults with hyperactivity of childhood onset." *The New England Journal of Medicine,* 1990; 323(20):1361-6.

> https://pubmed.ncbi.nlm.nih.gov/2233902/

Zanolli, Lauren. "Pesticides explained: the toxic chemicals in up to 70% of produce." *The Guardian,* May 29, 2019.

> https://www.theguardian.com/us-news/2019/may/29/pesticides-everyday-products-toxics-guide#:~:text=Residues%20are%20in%20up%20to, advocacy%20group%20Environmental%20Working%20Group

# ENDNOTES

1. Vagg, Richard. *The Brain.* The History Channel, 2009.
2. Makary, Marty. *The Price We Pay: What Broke American Health Care--and How to Fix It,* (New York, NY: Bloomsbury Publishing, 2019), 4.
3. Amen, Daniel, Brain Health Professional Certification Course, Module 2: "Opening The Mind, Healing The Brain," Lesson 1: "The Critical Importance of Brain SPECT Imaging in Psychiatric Practice," accessed March 15, 2022; Daniel Amen, et al, "Specific ways brain SPECT imaging enhances clinical psychiatric practice," Journal of Psychoactive Drugs, April - June 2012.
4. Grubin, David. *The Secret Life of the Brain: The Child's Brain,* PBS, 2005.
5. Amen, Daniel, "Brain Health Professional Certification Course," Module 2: "Introduction"; Daniel Amen, *HIGH PERFORMANCE BRAINS, Disc 1,* (MindWorks, 2012); Amen, Daniel, *Magnificent Mind At Any Age,* (New York, NY: Three Rivers Publishing Group, 2008).
6. Amen, Daniel, *High Performance Brains,* Disc 1; David Grubin, *The Secret Life of the Brain: The Teenage Brain,* PBS, 2005.
7. Merrill, Scott. "Legal Field Has High Rates of Substance Abuse, Mental Illness," *New Hampshire Bar News,* July 19, 2021; Priscilla Henson, "Addiction & Substance Abuse in Lawyers: Statistics to Know," American Addiction Centers, March 22, 2022.
8. Henson, Priscilla, MD. "Addiction & Substance Abuse in Lawyers: Statistics to Know." American Addiction Centers, March 22, 2022.
9. Merrill, "Legal Field Has High Rates of Substance Abuse, Mental Illness."
10. Amen, Daniel. *High Performance Brains,* Disc 1; Daniel Amen, *Change Your Brain, Change Your Body,* (New York, NY: Harmony Books, 2010), 4; Amen, *Magnificent Mind At Any Age,* 13.
11. Amen, Daniel, *Change Your Brain, Change Your Life,* (New York, NY: Three Rivers Publishing Group, 1998), 13; Grubin, David. *The Secret Life of the Brain: The Teenage Brain.*
12. Amen, Daniel, *Brain Health Professional Certification Course, Lesson 1 & 2.*

13. Amen, Daniel, *Change Your Brain, Change Your Body*, 18; Amen, *Magnificent Mind At Any Age*, 13.

14. Sapolsky, Robert. "Stress and Your Body," Lecture 13: "Stress, Learning and Memory." (Chantilly, VA: The Teaching Company, 2010) Stanford University, Menlo Park, CA.

15. Domonell, Kristen. "This Is Your Body On Fear," UW Medicine, October 25, 2017; "Fight-or-Flight Reaction." *ChangingMinds.org*.

16. Amen, *Change Your Brain, Change Your Body*, 111, 237.

17. Amen, *Magnificent Mind At Any Age*, 31.

18. Amen, *High Performance Brains*, Disc 1; Amen, "Change Your Brain, Change Your Body," 237.

19. Amen, *Magnificent Mind At Any Age*, 31; Amen, *Change Your Brain, Change Your Body*, 111; Sapolsky, "Stress and Your Body," Lecture 13: "Stress, Learning and Memory."

20. Goleman, Daniel. *Social Intelligence: The New Science of Human Relationships* (New York, NY, Bantam, 2006), 268.

21. "Dopamine." *Wikipedia*, accessed September 20, 2020.

22. Rosling, Claire. "Serotonin: A Molecule of Happiness," University of Bristol, UK, accessed September 20, 2020.

23. Nicholson, Christie. "No Fair! My Serotonin Level Is Low," *Scientific American*, June 9, 2008.

24. Conrad Stoppler, Melissa. "Endorphins: Natural Pain and Stress Fighters." *MedicineNet*, accessed October 1, 2020.

25. Ibid.

26. Goleman, *Social Intelligence*, 40; Amen, Daniel, *Healing the Hardware of the Soul*, Disc 2.

27. Sapolsky, *Stress and Your Body*, Lecture 7: "Stress, Growth and Child Development."

28. Goleman, Daniel. *Emotional Intelligence* (New York: Bantam, 1995), 178.

29. Dr. Siegel, Ronald. *The Science of Mindfulness, Lecture 2*.

30. Goleman, *Social Intelligence*, 230.

31. Ibid.

32. Ibid.

33. Goleman, *Social Intelligence*, 230; Malcolm Gladwell, *Blink* (Little, Brown, and Co., New York, NY, 2005), 224-228.

34. Goleman, *Social Intelligence*, 232.

35. Gladwell, Malcolm. *Blink* (Little, Brown, and Co., New York, NY, 2005), 224-228.

36. Goleman, *Social Intelligence*, 227-229; Heminway, John. *Stress: Portrait of a Killer*. National Geographic, 2008; "Whitehall Study." *Wikipedia*, accessed April 30, 2012.

37. Sapolsky, *Stress and Your Body,* Lecture 18: "Psychological Modulators of Stress." Stanford University.

38. Sapolsky, *Stress and Your Body,* Lecture 2: "The Nuts and Bolts."

39. Heminway, John. *Stress: Portrait of a Killer.*

40. Ibid.

41. Norden, Jeanette. *Understanding The Human Brain:* Lecture 35: "Wellness and the Brain" (Chantilly, VA: The Teaching Company, 2007). Vanderbilt University School of Medicine.

42. Goleman, *Social Intelligence,* 228-229; Heminway, John. *Stress: Portrait of a Killer.*

43. Goleman, *Emotional Intelligence,* 139.

44. Ibid.

45. Goleman, *Social Intelligence,* 228-229; Heminway, John. *Stress: Portrait of a Killer;* Sapolsky, *Stress and Your Body,* Lecture 10: "Stress and Your Immune System"; Huan Song, Fang Fang, Gunnar Tomasson, et al, "Association of Stress-Related Disorders With Subsequent Autoimmune Disease," *JAMA,* June 19, 2018,

46. Sapolsky, *Stress and Your Body,* Lecture 10: "Stress and Your Immune System."

47. Ibid.

48. Sapolsky, *Stress and Your Body,* Lecture 10: "Stress and Your Immune System"; Innate Immune System, *Wikipedia,* accessed February 21, 2021.

49. Goleman, *Social Intelligence,* 228-229; Heminway, John. *Stress: Portrait of a Killer;* Sapolsky, *Stress and Your Body,* Lecture 2: "The Nuts and Bolts."

50. Goleman, *Emotional Intelligence,* 178.

51. Goleman, *Social Intelligence,* 229-230.

52. Ibid.

53. Goleman, *Social Intelligence,* 235-236.

54. Ibid.

55. Norden, *Understanding The Human Brain:* Lecture 35: "Wellness and the Brain"; Sapolsky, *Stress and Your Body,* Lecture 10: "Stress and Your Immune System."

56. Stojanovich, Ljudmila, and Marisavljevich, Dragomir. "Stress as a trigger of *autoimmune disease,"* Autoimmunity Reviews, November 29, 2007.

57. Heminway, John. *Stress: Portrait of a Killer.*

58. Heminway, John. *Stress: Portrait of a Killer;* Sapolsky, *Stress and Your Body,* Lecture 16: "Stress and Aging."

59. Heminway, John. *Stress: Portrait of a Killer.*

60. Ibid.

61. Ibid.

62. Goleman, *Social Intelligence,* 273; Sapolsky, *Stress and Your Body,* Lecture 13: "Stress, Learning and Memory."

63. LeDoux, Joseph. *The Emotional Brain* (New York: Simon and Schuster, 1996), 122; Norden, *Understanding The Human Brain*: Lecture 35: "Wellness and the Brain"; Goleman, *Social Intelligence*, 268.

64. LeDoux, *The Emotional Brain*, 64-68.

65. LeDoux, *The Emotional Brain*, 122; Norden, *Understanding The Human Brain*: Lecture 35: "Wellness and the Brain"; Goleman, *Social Intelligence*, 268.

66. Gates, Donna. "Stress and Coping: A Model for the Workplace," *AAOHN Journal*, Volume: 49 issue: 8, 390-398, August 1, 2001; Sauter, Steven, et al. "STRESS...At Work." The National Institute for Occupational Safety and Health, 1999: 99-101.

67. Ibid.

68. Reinberg, Steven. "Surgical Tools Too Often Left Behind in Patients." HealthDay Reporter, WebMD, October 17, 2013.

69. Ibid.

70. Goleman, *Social Intelligence*, 268.

71. Norden, *Understanding The Human Brain*: Lecture 35: "Wellness and the Brain"; Goleman, *Social Intelligence*, 268.

72. Grubin, David. *The Secret Life of the Brain: The Aging Brain*, PBS, 2005.

73. Amen. *Change Your Brain, Change Your Body*, 17.

74. Siegel. *The Science of Mindfulness*, Lecture 2.

75. Ibid.

76. Rawlence, Christopher. *Secrets of the Mind*, NOVA, 2001.

77. "Military Suicide Rates Are at an All-Time High; Here's How We're Trying to Help," United Service Organizations, September 1, 2021.

78. Goleman, *Social Intelligence*, 150.

79. Ibid.

80. LeDoux, Joseph. *Synaptic Self: How Our Brains Become Who We Are* (New York: Penguin Books, 2003), 45.

81. Ibid.

82. Hamilton, Ryan. *How You Decide: The Science of Human Decision Making* (Chantilly, VA: The Teaching Company, 2007); Amen, *Magnificent Mind At Any Age*, 13.

83. LeDoux, *Synaptic Self: How Our Brains Become Who We Are*, 45.

84. Grubin, *The Secret Life of the Brain: The Aging Brain*.

85. Heminway, John. *Stress: Portrait of a Killer*.

86. Ibid.

87. Norden, *Understanding The Human Brain*: Lecture 26, "Brain Plasticity."

88. Heminway, John. *Stress: Portrait of a Killer. National Geographic, 2008;* LeDoux. *Synaptic Self: How Our Brains Become Who We Are*, 67.

89. LeDoux, *Synaptic Self: How Our Brains Become Who We Are*, 67-68.

90. Ibid.

91. Goleman, *Social Intelligence, 78*

92. Goleman, *Social Intelligence,* 79; LeDoux, *Synaptic Self: How Our Brains Become Who We Are,* 299.

93. LeDoux, *Synaptic Self: How Our Brains Become Who We Are,* 299.

94. Taylor, Victoria "Unhappy in America: Nearly 70% of U.S. employees miserable at work, study finds," *New York Daily News,* January 28, 2015.

95. Clarisse Levitan. "Why 85% of People Hate their Jobs," Staff Squared, December 3, 2019,

96. Clifton, Jim. "The World's Broken Workplace," Gallup, June 13, 2017.

97. "Workplace Violence," United States Department of Labor, Occupational Safety and Health Administration, accessed January 28, 2022.

98. "Stress in America 2020: A National Mental Health Crisis." APA, 2020, accessed January 7, 2022.

99. Ibid.

100. Ibid.

101. Amen, *Change Your Brain, Change Your Body,* 154-155.

102. Amen, *Change Your Brain, Change Your Body,* 147.

103. Ibid.

104. Amen, *Magnificent Mind At Any Age,* 217.

105. Amen, *Magnificent Mind At Any Age,* 218.

106. Amen, *Magnificent Mind At Any Age,* 219.

107. Rawlence, *Secrets of the Mind.*

108. Amen, *Change Your Brain, Change Your Body,* 257-258.

109. Amen, *Change Your Brain, Change Your Body,* 224; *Christopher Rawlence, Secrets of the Mind.*

110. Amen, *Change Your Brain, Change Your Body,* 223-226.

111. Ibid.

112. Ibid.

113. Ibid, 167.

114. Lock, S. "Statistics and Facts about the Fast Food Industry." Statista, 2016; "Five interesting facts about fast food." *Daily Journal,* November 16, 2019.

115. Spurlock, Morgan. *Fast Food and the Supersizing of America.* (New York, NY: Penguin Group (USA) Inc, 2005).

116. Diraddo, Danielle. "15 Surprising Facts and Statistics About The Fast Food Industry." Toast, 2021

117. Ibid.

118. Woolston, Chris. "Type 2 Diabetes and Kids: The Growing Epidemic." *Health Day,* May 15, 2022.

119. Spurlock.

120. French, Paul. "Fat China: how are policymakers tackling rising obesity?" *The Guardian*, February 12, 2015.

121. Gan, Nectar. "More than half of Chinese adults are now overweight. That's more people than the entire US population." CNN, December 24, 2020.

122. "The Looming National Security Crisis: Young Americans Unable to Serve in the Military," Heritage Foundation, February 13, 2018; Haltiwanger, John. "America Is So Out of Shape and Fat, It's Putting U.S. Army Soldiers in Danger," *Newsweek*, January 11, 2018; "US Military Officials Worried: Are Young Americans Too Fat?" *VOA News*, July 25, 2019.

123. Brooks, Sarah. "10 Shocking fast food facts." *SheKnows, sheknows.com*, July 1, 2013.

124. Amen, *Change Your Brain, Change Your Body*, 89-91.

125. Ibid.

126. Amen, *Change Your Brain, Change Your Body*, 90.

127. Ibid.

128. Amen, *Change Your Brain, Change Your Body*, 98.

129. Amen, *Change Your Brain, Change Your Life*, 80-81.

130. Beurkens, Nicole. "Treating the Gut is Vitally Important for Autism Spectrum Disorders," *Holistic Child Psychology*, April 17, 2018.

131. Walsh, Bryan. "Getting Real About the High Price of Cheap Food." TIME Magazine, August 31, 2009; Kenner, Robert. *Food, Inc.* (Magnolia Home Entertainment, 2009).

132. McKay, Hannah. "Mega Farms Called CAFOs Dominate Animal Agriculture Industry." *Sentient Media*, September 29, 2021.

133. Ibid.

134. Ibid; Brockway, Ludo, Brockway, Otto. *Eating Our Way to Extinction.* (Broxstar Production, 2021).

135. McKay.

136. Entine, Jon. "FDA SpyGate -- New Revelations Challenge The New York Times Investigation of Agency 'Enemies List,' Raise More Questions About the 'Government's Most Dysfunctional Agency." *Forbes*, August 20, 2012.

137. Kenner.

138. McKay.

139. "Are Pesticides in Foods Harming Your Health?" *Healthline*, medically reaccessed on May 26, 2021.

140. Zanolli, Lauren. "Pesticides explained: the toxic chemicals in up to 70% of produce." *The Guardian*, May 29, 2019.

141. Amen, *Change Your Brain, Change Your Body*, 100.

142. Ibid.

143. Ibid.

144. Amen, *Magnificent Mind At Any Age*, 15, 72.

145. Amen, *Magnificent Mind At Any Age*, 32, 72.

146. Brockway, *Eating Our Way to Extinction*.

147. Ibid.

148. Bouchez, Colette. "Good Fat, Bad Fat: The Facts About Omega-3: Think all dietary fat is the same? Guess again." *WebMD*, December 12, 2008.

149. Ibid.

150. Ibid.

151. Covington, Maggie. "Omega-3 Fatty Acids." *American Family Physician.* 2004 Jul 1;70(1):133-40

152. Amen, *Change Your Brain, Change Your Body*, 92.

153. Amen, *Magnificent Mind At Any Age*, 72.

154. Kenner, Robert. *Food, Inc.* (Magnolia Home Entertainment, 2009).

155. "Dirt Poor: Have Fruits and Vegetables Become Less Nutritious?" *Earth Talk. The Scientific American*, April 27, 2011.

156. Fletcher, Robert and Kathleen Fairfield, MD, DrPH. "Vitamins for Chronic Disease Prevention in Adults." *JAMA*, June 19, 2002.

157. Amen, *Change Your Brain, Change Your Body*, 18, 86; Amen, *High Performance Brains*, Disc 4.

158. Amen, *Change Your Brain, Change Your Body*, 99.

159. Amen, *Change Your Brain, Change Your Body*, 103.

160. Amen, *Magnificent Mind At Any Age*, 31-32.

161. Amen, *High Performance Brains, Disc 1;* Sapolsky, *Stress and Your Body*, Lecture 15: "Stress, Seep and Lack of Sleep."

162. Ibid.

163. Hamilton, Ryan. *How You Decide: The Science of Human Decision Making.* The Great Courses, Chantilly, VA: The Teaching Company, 2007.

164. Ibid. Bradberry, Travis and Jean Greaves. *The Emotional Intelligence Quick Book.* New York: Fireside, 2005, *120–21. See also Goleman, Emotional Intelligence, 26.*

165. Hamilton. *How You Decide: The Science of Human Decision Making.*

166. Amen, *Change Your Brain, Change Your Body*, 110; Amen, *Magnificent Mind At Any Age*, 28; Grubin, *The Secret Life of the Brain: The Teenage Brain.*

167. Amen, *Change Your Brain, Change Your Body*, 110; Amen, *Magnificent Mind At Any Age*, 28; Grubin, *The Secret Life of the Brain: The Aging Brain*; Sapolsky, *Stress and Your Body*, Lecture 13: "Stress, Learning and Memory."

168. Amen, *Change Your Brain, Change Your Life*, 78-79; "Can Exercise Make Me High?" *HealthCentral.com*, September 17, 2001. Adapted from Bailey, Covert and Bishop, Lea. *The Fit or Fat Woman.* Houghton Mifflin Company, 1989.

169. "Can Exercise Make Me High?" *HealthCentral.com*, accessed January 8, 2022.

170. Amen, *Change Your Brain, Change Your Life,* 78-79; Amen, *Change Your Brain, Change Your Body,* 111, 115.
171. Ibid.
172. "Exercise, positioning and lymphoedema." *Cancer Research UK,* accessed June 10, 2022.
173. Amen, *Change Your Brain, Change Your Body,* 111.
174. Amen, *Change Your Brain, Change Your Body,* 115.
175. Sparks, Dana. "TUESDAY Q & A: Establishing a daily routine first step for teen with chronic pain. Exercise takes the edge off chronic pain." Mayo Clinic, July 2, 2013.
176. *HealthCentral.com,* "Can Exercise Make Me High?"
177. Amen, *Change Your Brain, Change Your Life,* 78-79.
178. Daniel Amen, *The Masters Coaching Program, Lesson 1.*

# ABOUT THE AUTHORS

 Michael Warrick, MA, graduated with honors from The Ohio State University with his BA in psychology and with his master's degree from Roosevelt University in Clinical Psychology, graduating summa cum laude. He is currently working as a behavioral technician where he conducts behavioral therapy sessions with children and adolescents diagnosed with autism spectrum disorder.

Michael has extensive experience conducting and analyzing research in the area of autism spectrum disorder. His masters' thesis was on the relationships between neuropsychological test scores and high-functioning symptoms of autism spectrum disorder. Before that, he was involved in research related to executive functions in delusion proneness at The Ohio State University.

In addition to Michael's experience with research and working with individuals diagnosed with autism, he also has broad knowledge of neuroanatomy and how the functional and structural architecture of the brain correlate to behaviors.

Michael is currently preparing to continue with his education and earn his Ph.D. in Neuropsychology.

Scott Warrick, JD, MLHR, CEQC, SHRM-SCP (www.scottwarrick.com) is a two-time best-selling author, a national professional speaker, a practicing employment law attorney, and a human resource professional with 40 years of hands-on experience. Scott uses his unique background to help organizations get where they want to go, which includes coaching and training managers and employees in his own unique, practical, and entertaining style.

Scott trains managers and employees ON-SITE in over 50 topics. Scott travels the country presenting seminars on such topics as employment law, conflict resolution, and leadership and tolerance, to mention a few.

Scott combines the areas of law and human resources to help organizations in "Solving Employee Problems *BEFORE* They Start." Scott's goal is *NOT* to win lawsuits. Instead, Scott's goal is to *PREVENT THEM* while improving *EMPLOYEE MORALE.*

Scott's first book, *Solve Employee Problems Before They Start: Resolving Conflict in the Real World,* is a #1 Best Seller for Business and Conflict Resolution on Amazon. It was also named by EGLOBALIS as one of the best global Customer and Employee books for 2020-2021. Scott's most recent book, *Living The Five Skills of Tolerance: A User's Manual For Today's World,* is also a #1 Best Seller in 13 categories on Amazon.

Scott has been named one of Business First's 20 People To Know In HR, CEO Magazine's 2008 Human Resources "Superstar," a Nationally Certified Emotional Quotient Counselor (CEQC) and a SHRM National Diversity Conference Presenter in 2003, 2006,

2007, 2008, 2010, and 2012. Scott has also received the Human Resource Association of Central Ohio's Linda Kerns Award for Outstanding Creativity in the Field of HR Management and the Ohio State Human Resource Council's David Prize for Creativity in HR Management.

Scott's academic background and awards include Capital University College of Law (Class Valedictorian, first out of 233, and Summa Cum Laude), Master of Labor & Human Resources and BA in Organizational Communication from The Ohio State University.

Scott can be reached at scott@scottarrick.com or through his website at www.scottwarrick.com